Blue Ridge Mountain

HERITAGE

A Caricature of Southern Appalachian Life

by Roy Owenby

Catch the Spirit of Appalachia, Inc.
WESTERN NORTH CAROLINA

FIRST EDITION 2014

Layout/edited/images by Amy Ammons Garza

Other Books by Roy Owenby
"The Owl Knows," an Appalachian Trail Mystery 2012

For additional copies of these books
please go to CSAbooks.com

Publisher:
Catch the Spirit of Appalachia, Inc.—Imprint of:
Ammons Communications — SAN NO. 8 5 1 – 0 8 8 1
29 Regal Avenue • Sylva, North Carolina 28779
Phone/fax: (828) 631-4587

Library of Congress Control Number: 2014940668

ISBN No. 978-0-9913803-4-3

PRINTED IN THE UNITED STATES OF AMERICA

Dedication

To Merritt Fouts
Principal, Educator, Country Gentleman
Owner and Editor of "The Burningtown News"

And

Roy M. Owenby, Sr. and Gladys Dills Owenby
The best parents a man ever had

And

To Nita, my wife, friend and inspiration

Table of Contents

Table of Contents

Table of Contents

GHOSTS, HAINTS AND FLYING SAUCERS

A HUNTING WE WILL GO

PREACHERS AND SINNERS

Table of Contents

PROLOGUE

Waterfall Memories

Quietly, I sat on the rocks I had stockpiled to make a set of steps down the bank from the road. About ten feet below me, the little waterfall gurgled and babbled. It wasn't very high, only about a foot above the bottom of the brook, but its size didn't matter. It was the memories it elicited as the soothing sound sang to me from the past. I struggled to find words that would describe the feelings created deep in my psyche. I was trapped in the wonderment of the magical sounds that emanated from the little pool as the cold mountain water splashed on the rocks. I gave in to the allure of the waterfall's song and sat mesmerized by the hypnotic drumbeat that drew me away from my intended task.

I had spent hours removing the briars, weeds and shrubs concealing the little brook that had been my mother's pride and joy. A few yards upstream lay the remnants of an old oak that had stood proudly over the spring for seventy-five years. It had fallen across the brook a few years back, but thoughts of hauling it away still tugged at my heart.

In my mind's eye, I pictured the tree as it was when I was eight years old. Its girth had been over eight feet and it had stood proud and strong for all those years. It was almost like remembering a loved one. My little sister and I had played around that tree many times. One limb had been parallel to the ground, a foot in diameter where it grew out from the tree. Dad had hooked up a tire swing from that limb, giving us fun and pleasure for many a summer afternoon. I don't know what happened to the swing or when it disappeared. It was there when we moved away, and years later, when I returned, it was gone. When we moved, I felt like a shrub that had been uprooted and carried across the world. At that age, no one asked my opinion; we just went where Dad had regular work. I suppose if the choice had been mine, I would have elected to stay. But if I had, the world would not have been my oyster. Many times, things work out for the best even if we don't want to believe it at the time.

As I continued to stare at the little waterfall, its peaceful tune played to my heart; still captivating and oh, so restful. I could see Mom and Dad sitting on the porch after a hard day's work. Mom always wanted to sit close to Dad so she would push her chair up next to his. It never worked the other way around. Dad worked hard, loved his wife and children, but he certainly wasn't a sentimentalist. The homemade wooden chairs were made for utility, not to impress. The seats were made from dried strips of hickory bark. The outer bark had been pulled away and the inside was sturdy and durable with a little stretch. I believe the chairs were made by my Great-Uncle John.

In those days, Dad smoked Country Gentlemen or Prince Albert tobacco. I can still see him leaning over in that chair rolling his own. Once in a while, he liked to show off and roll it with one hand. He would take out a match, pass it rapidly down the side of his pants leg, and the friction would cause it to light. I think I was in the Navy before I mastered that trick. Dad would then lean back in his chair and enjoy his smoke. Mom would stand up, move her chair a couple feet away from Dad until he finished smoking, and then she would move back. If he even noticed; I wasn't aware of it.

Sometimes Dad would sit on the porch and read his Bible. Mom read hers a lot also, but she usually read it in the house. Dad would keep a little pocket notebook handy, and he would make notes about scripture verses which he thought needed additional study. When he finished reading, he would go into the house, bring his old concordance out and begin to analyze the notes he had made. He knew a great deal about the Bible and he certainly believed in it, but he wasn't narrow-minded about it. I do know he constantly strived to increase his Biblical wisdom. He wasn't afraid to ask questions, and he wasn't afraid of the answers. To this day, his wisdom lives within me.

When Grandma and Great-Uncle John were younger, they would come to visit in the cool of the evening after they had eaten. They would sit on the porch and talk about the weather, farming, politics and religion. Sometimes, Grandma was hardnosed about religion so Dad would be careful not to upset her. He knew which side of his bread to butter.

People walked most of the time in those days and they weren't usually in a hurry. If my aunts, cousins or neighbors happened to walk by, it was considered bad manners not to stop and chat a bit. Mom and Dad would stop whatever they were doing and enjoy their company. There was no electricity in Nantahala, so there was no television. A few people had battery-powered radios but the batteries were saved for important programs like the Grand Ole Oprey on Saturday night.

It was hard to leave the little waterfall and return to reality. It had been there since the early days of the Cherokee, I'm sure. Grandma Rosa and Grandpa Henry had lived there before Mom and Dad. It holds many secrets as it gurgles and bubbles day-after-day around the clock. Some would say it's just an inanimate object, but I know better. It's the keeper of a little piece of my Blue Ridge Mountain heritage and it was created by God. These days, men often make false waterfalls, but only God can make one like mine. All those years, it waited in the weeds and bushes for me to return. I gave it sunlight again, and it brightened my day. In today's language, that's called a win-win.

CHAPTER ONE
Child of the Appalachians

Praise the Lord & Pass the Taters

My roots are firmly planted in the Appalachian Mountains. Love and appreciation for this region and its people are a part of my heritage that is inseparable from my heart and mind. My language and speech are a direct result of the grammar and syntax developed by my forefathers and passed down generation by generation. Mountain people learned to communicate with each other in their own way with little regard to so-called proper English. Because they were isolated from the outside world, they developed their own synonyms, euphemisms and metaphors and passed them on to each other as they worked and worshiped together.

I can still remember Aunt Elva Morgan saying she "was yanked up by the hair on her head." Now, she didn't mean that Grandma Rosa was mean to her. She simply meant that she was raised in abject poverty. "Over yonder" was a term my mom and my aunts used regularly. This term apparently is not used outside the South. It is actually correct English. Now, a great many of the Southern sayings and words were not correct grammar or spelling but were clearly understood by other Southern folk.

Mother would say, "If you don't stop that crying, I'm going to give you something to cry about." Literally, this term has a double meaning, but figuratively, we kids knew when she said that, "it was time to dry up."

Mother had a habit of going out on the back porch to throw out her dishwater. Invariably, she left the door open even if it was the middle of January. Dad would say, "Gladys, for God sakes, shut that pneumonia hole."

Sometimes, Dad would go out the door, and Mom would say, "Where you goin' Roy?" And Dad would reply, "I'm fixin' to go down the road apiece." Sometimes the question would irk him, and he would say, "Tain't none of yer business, Gladys." They didn't argue much in front of us kids, but I knew she would "light into him" when he got back.

My cousin, Christine, lived with us for a while. I wish I had a dollar for every time she said, "Well, I'll swaney." She couldn't bring herself to say "I'll be darned." That was too close to a swear word. The men would sometimes say swear words, but never in front of the ladies. Somehow, I can't picture my dad whacking his thumb with a hammer and saying, "Well, I'll swaney." ·

Another favorite swear word was "tarnation" or "Sam Hill." "What in Sam Hill did you mean by that?" My Aunt Lucy would say, "Lord in Heaven help me, what is that child into now?"

We would go to visit someone, and my mom would say, "Now, act like you've got some raisin'."

I remember one of my aunts talking about another woman when she thought I wasn't listening; "She's a good ol' soul, but she ain't got a lick of sense." Or she would say when one of her kids was misbehaving; "He's having a dying duck fit; I'm going in there and box his ears." Another favorite was, "I'm gonna jerk a knot is his tail." Or one of them would say, "Sissy, put down your dress, I can see to the promise land."

When we went to church, we would put on our "Sunday go-to-meetin' clothes" which, in my case, was a clean pair of overalls. We had a neighbor that drank a lot, and my dad would say, "He's just downright sorry."

I can remember my Aunt Frances telling me, "Lordie Mercy, son, I ain't seen you in a month-of-Sundays."

My Uncle John would say that something smelled so bad "that it would knock a buzzard off a gut wagon."

And of course, the one I hated, "Son, go cut me a switch."

Sometimes, I would ask my grandma how she was doing, and she would say, "Son, I'm wore to a frazzle," or she would say, "I feel like I've been chewed up and spit out." If someone got into trouble, my Aunt Velma would say, "Lie down with a dog and you'll get fleas." Another one when the kids were rowdy, "A body can't get a minute's peace around here." And then there was, "bless your pea-picking heart," or crooked as a dog's hind leg," or "finer n' frog hair" and finally, "don't go gittin yourself all gussied up."

My ol' Navy buddy from Robbinsville would say, "Look at him grinning like a hinny eatin' sawbrars." Some guy asked him once what sawbrars were, and he said, "You ain't from the South, are you boy?" Someone asked him once what his girlfriend looked like, and he said, "She's so ugly she could haunt a house." I found out later, that she had sent him a "Dear John" letter, and he wasn't feeling too charitable that day.

Dogs were very much a part of farm life when I was growing up. When we would see a pretty girl, we would say, "She's cuter than a speckled pup." Another one was, "I'm hungrier than a hound dog suckin' pups." One of the ladies on my work shift in Boone had a bunch of mountain sayings. "It'll be a dark night at the well before he'll get a drink," meaning he was too ugly for her to date in the daylight.

One night, she asked me to help with her machine. I asked her to describe the problem. "I'm a stuck duck in a dry pond," she said. In other words, she couldn't figure out why her machine wouldn't wind the wire properly. Another one was, "Don't just sit there like a frog on a log." She would come in to work and say, "I was in sich a hurry that I gave my hair a lick and a promise." People were either "fair to middlin" or "full of beans," depending on whether she liked them or not. This was in the mini-skirt days, and one day a young woman passed her machine. "She's as naked as a picked chicken," she told me.

One day, she came in and told me that she had been to a dance the night before. "I ain't had so much fun since the hog ate my brother-in-law," she said. About one of her co-workers; "She ain't got much snap in her garters." "I'm so hungry, I could eat the south end of a north bound skunk," was another one of her favorites. Regarding another one of her co-workers who weighed in at about ninety pounds. "She's about as big as a bar of soap after a hard day's washing."

Someone who was confused or mixed up "didn't know daylight from dark." A child was often described as being "knee high to a grasshopper." She's madder than a wet hen" was often used. Someone who was a little less than sane "didn't have both oars in the water." A hyperactive child was "as wild as a June bug on a string." Someone who was happy about something was "plumb tickled." A good host would hand you a cup of coffee and say, "It's already been saucered and blowed." Someone who thought you were handing them a line would say, "My cow died last night so I don't need your bull." A good joke would "tickle your funny bone." If something went wrong, "someone throwed a clod in the churn." And finally, one of my favorites from Tennessee Ernie Ford about a girl who was scared; "Her eyes looked like two buck-eyes in a barrel of buttermilk."

I could go on with this "until the cows come home," but you "get my drift." A lot of us here in the mountains still use many of these expressions. They're so common to us that we really don't notice it when our friends and neighbors use them. I used to drive my college professors "over the cliff" with them.

I especially like to use them around people who are "trying to put on the dog." Come to think of it, I'm not sure I could stop using countrified expressions, but that's probably because I don't want to.

Now, I know this is difficult for you citified folk, but "just grin and bear it." A little "larnin" never hurt anybody so "give it your best shot." After all, Southern colloquialisms get straight to the point. They are, in fact, an efficient way to communicate. After all, "why go around your elbow to get to your thumb?"

A Child's Quest for Knowledge

B ack in the '40s and '50s, Nantahala kids were not privy to adult information, and the schools didn't teach any kind of sex education. Farm kids had a small edge over town kids because they observed first hand the life cycles of farm animals. Even so, they often did not relate this information to humans. My grandmother told her girls that babies were found in a stump. My Mom said she believed that story until she was fourteen. It was in this kind of climate that I learned to be curious and inquisitive. In other words, I was nosy.

It wasn't the kind of nosy that gossipers are, but a little kid's quest for knowledge. My Mom's sisters and older nieces would come over for a visit, and in a short time, they would start talking about important stuff. At some point, Mom would say, "Son, why don't you go out and play." Even at age five or six, I figured out that some important information was about to change hands. One day, I was playing under the house, and quite by accident, I was sitting in a location where I could hear the conversation above me.

As I listened intently, I thought, wow, this is some good stuff. Because I was a little boy, I didn't understand a lot of it, but still, it was new stuff I hadn't heard before. Sitting in my listening spot became a regular thing. Over time, I began to piece together all that information I wasn't allowed to hear. For example, I learned that my older cousin wasn't getting fat; she was going to have a baby. Now, my dad was one of the most discreet men I've ever known, and I inherited that trait from him. In other words, there was still stuff I didn't understand, but there was no one I could ask. It was hard-wired in my genes to be circumspect.

Later, we moved away, and my good listening spot was lost forever. Now, I had no option but to come up with new ways to gather adult information that I wasn't allowed to know. When we moved to our house on Camp Branch, I soon figured out that I could sit on top of the house and hear through the stove pipe. It worked even better when I left the stove door slightly open. In the summertime, no one noticed because there wasn't a fire in the stove.

My Dad and my Uncle John talked about some good stuff, too. When they met down by the barn, I would sneak in the back and hide in the loft. I soon learned that men talked about different stuff than women did, or at least, they talked about it in different ways. Each of the conversations I overheard was a piece of a puzzle, and over time, I began putting the puzzle together. When I played with my cousins, they would ask each other questions, and I would know the answer, but I couldn't tell without revealing my sources. I became especially close-mouthed when I learned that one of my cousins got a good thrashing for eavesdropping.

When Dad and I walked to Weaver Cochran's store, he would stop off along the way and talk to the men he knew, and he knew them all. Dad didn't have much formal education, but he loved to talk, and he knew a lot about different subjects.

The first stop was usually at Amos Grant's house. Amos would come out, and they would stand out by the corn crib and share information. I would pretend to look for thunder puppies in the branch and then sneak around behind the corn crib. Now, Amos and Flossie had thirteen children, and it stood to reason that a man with that many kids would be a fountain of knowledge.

On down the road we would go until we got to Uncle David and Uncle Golie's house. Now, there wasn't any place to eavesdrop there, so I would walk a little ways down the road and throw rocks at something, usually a tree. I didn't throw rocks at mailboxes since I had already gotten a good whipping for that earlier. I would pretend disinterest while listening intently. It was easier to get away with my foolishness with the men than with the women. The ladies were more cautious. Be that as it may, when they thought no one was around, they would really spread the butter on the bread. They knew a lot more about childbearing stuff than the men did, but I guess that's because they had more firsthand knowledge.

One of my favorite stops was at Uncle Phillip Passmore's house. Phillip wasn't really my uncle; he was one of those men who invariably becomes every-body's uncle. At least, it was like that in those days. Uncle Phillip was sort of looked up to by the men in the Nantahala community. He was one of those wise old men who had been around the horn several times. He was also a preacher; farmer, mechanic, and he read a lot. He talked loud too, and that made it easier to gather information as I threw rocks off below the road.

Uncle Phillip always had a Farmer's Almanac, and he was an excellent source of information on the weather. Between the almanac and his considerable knowledge of weather in past years, he could predict the weather better than anyone. At least everybody thought he could. If Uncle Phillip had something he really didn't want me to hear, all he had to do was get Aunt Elender to offer me some food. I would follow her in the house for a slice of hot buttered cornbread or a biscuit with sorghum molasses dripping out the sides.

The final stop, of course, was Weaver Cochran's store. Weaver saw everybody in the Nantahala com-munity at one time or another. Everybody would tell him news, and he would impart the knowledge to other customers as they came in. Since there were no telephones or electricity, the community stores be-came the local news station. If somebody had a new baby, Weaver knew it. If a farmer's horse died, Weaver had the information. If somebody's barn burned down, Weaver had already been told. It was also nice that I didn't have to eavesdrop; Weaver told everybody everything. If the news was really adult stuff, he would look around to see how close the nearest kid was and then lower his voice. Of course, I would start inspecting the pickle barrel or eying the penny candy like I had no interest in the conversation at all.

When I was about fifteen years old, Mom goaded Dad into having a father/son talk with me. Apparently, Mom thought I believed newborn babies were found in stumps like she did when she was that age. Dad was no fool; he knew I was already an expert in adult matters. We walked out through the field and talked. He had a way of putting me at ease. He said he had no doubt that I knew more than Mom did...and he was right, of course. By that time, he had realized I was as close-mouthed as he. He died with a lot of secrets he never told. I expect to do the same.

Supper at Grandma's House

At age five, we lived about two-tenths of a mile up the hill from my Grandmother Emma Owenby. I can vividly remember walking down the rutty old wagon road to her house. To my right, the steep wooded hills were resplendent in their autumn colors. Even as a young child, I could appreciate the golds, yellows and reds of the hardwood forest. Maple, poplar, sourwood, dogwood, sassafras and oaks covered the mountainside. To my left, Dad's and Grandma's two milk cows grazed in the big pasture, content with the sparse grass that covered the rocky hillside. Just above the barn, I climbed the bars that functioned as a gate. Adults would drop one end of two or three bars to go through but as a limber kid, I would just scramble over. Once inside the barn, I climbed the wooden ladder into the loft. I clambered over the loose hay to reach the other end. As I stood in the opening, I could see Grandma's old house with the ancient chestnut shingles covering the roof. I could see smoke rising out of the chimney and I knew Grandma was preparing a special supper. It seemed that I could never get enough to eat, and even then, it was a family joke about how much food I could put away at one sitting.

I jumped out of the loft onto a pile of hay I had put there on purpose to break my fall. It would have been much simpler just to climb back down but it wasn't nearly as much fun. I ran on down the rutty wagon track avoiding the rocks as I went. At that age I was quick and agile and even if I fell, I would just jump up and laugh about it. I didn't fall, though. I made it to Grandma's yard in a dead run. She sat on the porch waiting for me, her floor-length dress draped around her legs. I could see her worn but comfortable high-button shoes jutting out from under her dress.

Her wrinkled face lit up and she smiled like only a grandmother can. I knew she loved me, and I certainly doted on her. She knew that food was the best way to spoil me...she knew what I liked and how to prepare it. We talked for a few minutes before she stood and asked me to come into the house. My mouth watered as I thought about the delicious food awaiting me.

Grandma went to the hearth and lifted the lid off her big iron pot. I could smell the stew all the way across the room. She had cooked it to perfection, a little too done for most people, but the way we both liked it. I don't remember what it had in it but I imagine it was pork with onions, tomatoes, potatoes and perhaps carrots. She went to the kitchen, brought back two bowls and ladled out the delicious stew, one bowl about half-full and one as full as she could safely carry. Without asking, I knew the full one was for me. She carried them to the kitchen table and placed them at ninety degrees from each other, her bowl closest to the stove and mine adjacent to the window. Next, she brought two plates and placed them next to the bowls. She turned and picked up the pan from the old wood stove and gave each of us a helping of polk salad. The delicious aroma almost took my breath away.

I sat in anticipation because I knew what was coming next. She carefully removed the wooden stick from under the handle on the oven door. The spring that kept it from dropping suddenly had been broken years before I was born. After she eased the door down, she picked up her old kitchen rags, spread them across her hands and carefully removed the pan from the oven. She placed it on the wooden board in the middle of the table so that she wouldn't burn her old oil tablecloth. The cracklin' bread smelled so good my stomach lurched. She looked over at me and smiled, knowing that I was watching, waiting for her to place a slab on my plate beside my poke salad. Then she sat down, bowed her head, placed her hands in supplication and silently asked her blessing. She never once asked me to do so but we both understood the importance of the ritual. Even at age five, I knew Grandma Emma was a devout Christian. I knew not to touch my food until she had finished the blessing. She raised her head and nodded, knowing it wasn't necessary to speak. Most people eat and then reach for their bread; I did just the opposite. Grandma's cracklin' bread tasted better than any rich man's food.

I bit off a big hunk, chewed on it for a bit and then spooned in stew and poke salad. To me, we were having a feast. Nobody could cook like Grandma except maybe my other Grandma. We ate in silence for a while, just enjoying ourselves. I continued to pack away the food until I felt like I would burst. When Grandma saw that I was about full, she started telling me about the two-headed snake she saw out by the hen house. I leaned back in my chair, satisfied and happy and prepared to listen to another of her tall tales. At that age, I believed them and it wasn't until later that I figured out that she was just entertaining me.

When we were finished, she got out her big dishpan, set it on the stove and packed our dishes in it. She poured hot water over them from a big enamel pot. She asked me if I wanted to walk down to Uncle Buddy's springhouse to get a dipper full of the clear cold water that perpetually ran out of the spout into the spring box. Once we had slaked our thirst, we walked past the house and up toward the little house where we lived. We stopped at the barn. By that time, Dad had brought in the cows and milked them. He gave Grandma her share. It began to get dark so Grandma headed back to her house but not before she gave me a big hug. Dad reached down and patted my stomach. "I see you made a pig of yourself again," he said. He tousled my hair and we headed uphill to prepare for bed. I remembered to think God for Grandma and her delicious food.

Dam Stories as Told by My Dad

When Dad decided to talk about his dam experiences, he would usually start off by saying that he helped back up a lot of dam water. Even though he used the word in the correct context, Mom would jump his case saying he was just finding a sneaky way to cuss. Of course, he knew in advance this would get her riled so he enjoyed every minute of it. He was proud of the work he did for the TVA and Nantahala Power and Light even though the work was so-called common labor. He was never fired and never laid off from any job. I know he was a hard worker and his immediate bosses appreciated him and said so many times. Unfortunately, that didn't do much to raise his pay; but still, one likes to be appreciated.

Dad got a job working on the Nantahala Dam project (Aquone) in early 1940. This was before World War II; however, Dad said most everybody knew we were going to get pulled into the war. In earlier years, a smaller dam had been planned further upstream, but the coming war was the primary motivator for a larger dam a little further downstream and this is the one that exists today. He and several of his relatives and friends worked there. He said there were some "Northerners" working on the site that were always stirring up trouble. Apparently, a bunch of locals, including him, ganged up around them one day and told them to straighten up or they would get themselves beat up. That quieted them down.

In his telling, he talked about how everybody worked hard day after day--grunt work, as he called it--digging ditches, laying pipe, removing stumps, pouring concrete, building forms and so on. I don't remember how much he was paid but I'm sure it was less than ten cents an hour. I know he wasn't happy about the loss of the Aquone Community because he had friends there who were hurting about being forced to move. He also thought it was a desecration to dig up the cemeteries. Later, he helped dig a tunnel through the mountain that was destined to deliver water from White Oak Creek to the Nantahala powerhouse. I asked him if he was scared working back in a hole in the mountain, and he said he never thought much about being afraid. He did say he didn't like working in the dark. "It just wasn't natural," he said.

I was barely two years old when the Fontana Dam was started. Whatever memory I have about it is what Dad told me. He went to work there after he left the Aquone project. He said the government man in charge acted like it had to be built in two weeks. Before long, there were men working around the clock. They threw up tents, shacks or whatever could be found to shelter the men. At some point, they asked him to be a foreman but he turned them down. "I didn't want to tell a bunch of knotheads what to do," he said and laughed about it. If I remember correctly, he started at ten cents an hour and before long, he was making thirteen cents an hour. He said the construction site was crazy, with men all over the place trying to do lots of different jobs and getting in each other's way.

About a year after they started, the builders began to pressure him to work on Sunday. He told them that he wouldn't work on the Sabbath. A short time later, they called everybody together and told them that they would have to work Sunday because the dam was a war effort. He said he went into the office, asked for his money and quit. As far as I know, he never worked on Sunday in his life. He believed that keeping the Ten Commandments was more important than supporting the war. He did support it, of course, but not in that way.

After that, Dad went back to cutting pulpwood for around seven cents an hour. (For you city folk, pulp wood is so-called softwoods--maple, birch, fir, spruce, poplar and pine). Because of the need for pulpwood for the war effort, he was given a deferment which he never asked for, and as a consequence, he never served in the military. He cut pulpwood in a variety of places, and I don't remember all of them. I know he worked on White Oak Creek, Cold Springs Creek, Rainbow Springs, Junaluska, Needmore and Tusquittee. Cutting pulpwood was hard work because it had to be done with an ax and a crosscut saw. No such thing as chainsaws in those days. They would stack the wood in cord stacks so the foreman would know how much they cut. Then it was hauled out of the woods on sleds or wagons pulled by horses, mules or oxen. It was hauled to the wood yard down in the Nantahala Gorge to be loaded in box cars. My Great-Uncle John and My Aunt Bessie often cooked in the wood camps.

I can't remember exactly when the Queens Creek Dam was started and finished. Bobby Queen told my cousin, Gail, that it was in 1948. I think it was begun in 1946 and finished in 1948. Dad worked on that dam for most of the duration. He took me across the Camp Branch Gap several times to watch the heavy equipment dig out clay and haul it to the dam site. Since I was a little kid with no worldly experience, those Ukes (huge dump trucks) looked monstrous to me.

We also went across the mountain above Raymond Wilson's place and crossed down to where we stood just above the dam site. All that activity, big machines and men doing all sorts of construction work really impressed me. Dad also worked on the pipeline that went down from the dam to the Beechertown Powerhouse. This was a very difficult job because the terrain was steep, rocky and dangerous. Rattlesnakes were commonplace. Dad was always proud of that accomplishment because it took a lot of skill and perseverance to build that pipeline. In his later years, he talked more about doing that job than any other.

Of course, these days, those dams have been in

service for 65-70 years. They have generated a lot of power for a lot of people. The lakes have provided fishing and boating recreation for thousands. Real estates agents and others have made a fortune selling lots to the gullible and/or well-heeled. It's just a shame so many people had to lose their homes, farms and family cemeteries so the dams could be built. This is called progress, sometimes properly and sometimes erroneously. We should never forget the sacrifices our forefathers made in our behalf. Of course, from a personal standpoint, I will always remember and appreciate Dad's dam experiences.

Biscuits and Gravy

Good biscuits and gravy are a gift from God. There is no way they just happened. It's obvious He created them through Godly mothers and grandmothers just as He created The Ten Commandments through Moses. Of course when it comes to good biscuits and gravy, science has been a total failure. Advanced weaponry, complex computers, yes, but there is no way to scientifically make good gravy. My grandmothers, mother and aunts would have laughed at using a recipe. They would have said in a heartbeat that it wouldn't work. Good gravy comes from the soul. My Grandmother Rosa could make better gravy half asleep than the world's greatest chefs could cobble together on their best days. She would take fatback grease, flour, milk, salt and pepper and perform this magic act that would have made Houdini jealous. When she had it, she would add a little country sausage that would make the gravy so good that it was almost a sin to eat it.

How she passed this ability on to her daughters is still a mystery to me. I doubt that she ever wrote down a recipe in her long life. Her daughters learned by osmosis; that is, Granny's recipes would flow from her brain cells across the room to her daughter's brain cells while they stood next to the stove and watched. The magic part was that every one of them could duplicate Grandma's cooking down to the smallest molecule.

Ditto with Grandma Emma. Back before my Aunt Alcie died, I showed up at her house about 7:00 a.m. This was no accident. When it comes to good food, I wasn't born yesterday. She wanted to know if I would like to have breakfast with her. I had called the day before and told her I would be there about 9:00 a.m.

"It's nothing fancy," she said, "just biscuits and gravy."

"I suppose I could," I said, trying to act surprised.

She wasn't born yesterday, either. She knew why I had gotten there early. She had enough for six people, and nobody lived there but her. I knew it was my solemn duty to eat for five, and I did. The smell alone was enough to make my stomach lurch. For some reason, I was salivating like a hungry Saint Bernard at a church picnic. The moment I stuck my fork into that cat head biscuit, the magic started. I closed my eyes and pictured the gravy made by Aunt Alcie's teacher, Grandma Emma. In my mind's eye, I could see the old lady cooking away on her wood stove. It had been about seventy years since Auntie had stood at that stove by Granny's knee. It had been fifty years since I had sat at Granny's table. The memories came tumbling out, and I almost cried. Some things can't be explained, they just are.

Over the years, I have scoured the country looking for restaurants that make good biscuits and gravy. I soon learned that the more upscale a restaurant, the worse they make gravy. That is, if they make it at all. The French are famous for their exotic gravies and sauces. I've been there and done that. They can't hold a light to the good country gravy made by a Western Carolina grandmother.

On one of my walkabouts, I stopped off at a little diner near Beckley, West Virginia. Naturally, I ordered biscuits and gravy. I'm the Duncan Hines of country breakfasts. The food was delicious. I called the waitress over and placed another order, twice. The third time, she looked at me like I was a glutton, but she went straight to the kitchen. I could only imagine what she told the cook. After I finished my sixth biscuit, I asked her if I could talk to the chef. After another funny look, she disappeared. I think she thought I was trying to bypass her, like going over her head. She returned and told me to go on back. I already knew who I would find. A little white-haired grandmother weighing in at about ninety-five pounds stood by the stove. She was at least eighty years old. She had a radiance about her that could only be understood by a connoisseur of country breakfasts. Her name was Maggie.

"I just wanted to tell you what a great cook you are," I said.

She blushed like only a grandmother can and said, "Thank you." We talked for several minutes. Her mother had taught her to cook. She was the youngest of ten children. I asked her if she had a recipe for her biscuits and gravy.

"You're pulling my leg," she said.

"I guess I am," I replied. "I recognized right away that you cook from the heart."

I ate there several times over a five year period. About three years ago, I rushed to get there before lunch started only to find that the restaurant had gone out of business. Realizing all good things eventually come to an end, I observed a moment of silence and drove on.

Way back when, my wife and kids went to the beach with some friends. At home alone, I decided to try a couple of recipes that I had found in a Southern cook book. I made a cake, and it was delicious. Next morning, I tried biscuits and gravy, from scratch naturally. I followed the recipes religiously. The biscuits could only be used for baseball practice, and the gravy tasted like it came out of a bag of potting soil. I put the plate on the floor for the dog. She sniffed at it and then looked at me like, "you're playing a practical joke on me, right!" So, I put the plate out in the backyard for the raccoon that had been raiding the trash cans. Next morning, the biscuits and gravy were still there. Right then, I decided my breakfast skills could be best used at a fast-food restaurant.

Like I said, all my aunts were great cooks, but my Aunt Ruby was the Emeril Lagasse of country cooking. She could put together a breakfast that only a master chef could assemble. She obviously paid attention while Grandma Rosa was cooking. I would walk five miles for one of her biscuits, and another five for the gravy on it. Of course, the biscuits and gravy were only a small part of her great breakfasts. She knew how to fry eggs that were too good to be true, and her homemade jelly was to die for. Every time I ate at her house, I made a pig of myself. Everybody knows that country mothers and grandmothers appreciate the biggest eaters, and I've always considered it my duty not to disappoint them.

Now, everyone who was raised by a country mother knows that God handed down the Ten Commandments to Moses on Mount Sinai. What everyone doesn't know is that God bypassed Moses when it came to the art of cooking. Somewhere on the American frontier, God passed down the recipe for biscuits and gravy. Mothers and grandmothers took it from there, and the rest is history. This leads me to believe there's a connection between Godly mothers and good biscuits and gravy. Usually, where you find one, you'll find the other, at least in the South.

Grubbing Stumps

When people clear a patch of woods to make a field today, they bring in a bulldozer and a trackhoe and demolish the trees and stumps in short order. A large trackhoe can jerk a good-sized stump out of the ground in about ten seconds. Sometimes I wish it wasn't that easy. The forests are diminishing at a rapid rate, animal habitats are being destroyed, and good farm land is going the way of the dinosaur.

Back in my grandfather's time, it was an entirely different matter. After the Civil War, my great-grandfather, Porter Owenby, and three of his five brothers moved to Nantahala from Gum Log, Georgia, which is between Blairsville and Murphy. Initially, they all moved to Briartown. The land they bought was all wooded. The road was atrocious; there were no doctors, nurses, grocery stores or any of the other amenities we modern folk enjoy. What they wanted with this particular land is beyond me, but they did, and they began improving it right away. I don't know specifically what they did to remove the trees in order to have pastures and fields, but I'm confident they used a combination of manual labor and horses or oxen.

Back then, when people removed trees, bushes and vines from land, they called it "grubbing." I have grubbed a stump, and it took me most of a day, so I can imagine how long it took my great-grandpa to clear several acres. The most backbreaking way to grub a stump is to do it manually. One takes a mattock, pick, shovel and ax and begins. Start out with the mattock and dig loose as much dirt as possible from around the roots. Often there are rocks, and they have to be removed also. Once the dirt is loosened, take a shovel and move the dirt out of the way. Repeat. When enough dirt and rocks are removed, take the ax and start cutting roots away. Continue this process until all the roots are removed or at least severed. If there is a taproot, it has to be cut loose which means one has to get under the stump. When a large stump is removed, it may take two or three men to push, roll or carry it away. Further back, people used acid, lye or even built a fire in the stump. That's how bad they hated grubbing.

If a farmer has a horse or an ox, the job was easier. A good horse could pull loose a small stump. A team of oxen could pull loose a medium size stump. Removing a large stump took a lot of manpower, horse and ox power. Bush could usually be grubbed out with a mattock by digging around the bush and pulling it loose. Larger bush had to be cut loose with a mattock or an ax. I remember watching my dad grub stumps, and it was a lot of work for him. He was a small man but very strong. I am five inches taller than he was, but I'm sure that I've never been as strong even though I go to the gym on a regular basis.

There was another way to remove stumps that worked very well, but was a little tricky and could be dangerous. It's a little stick about six inches long and one or two inches in diameter and it's called dynamite. Dad and my uncles called it "dannymite." Removing a stump with dynamite required an entirely different approach. This is the way Dad explained it.

One digs a small hole down under the stump and pushes the stick or sticks of dynamite down into it. One should be careful not to push too hard. After the dynamite is in the hole, pack some dirt around it. This helps concentrate the explosion and directs the energy into the stump instead of into the air. For example, just laying the stick beside a stump will mostly result in a lot on noise and a damaged stump. Blowing stumps out of the ground this way does take some experience to best direct the force properly. One should also not forget to have a good hiding place before the kabloey. Getting behind another stump or a tree is best or just run far enough away to be completely out of danger. Now, light the fuse and make tracks; don't stand around and wonder if the fuse is burning. Get behind cover immediately and even getting under cover is best. If the job has been done properly, pieces of stump will fly in all directions. It's not a good thing to get hit in the head with a forty pound root. Once the noise is over and all the pieces stop flying, pick up the stump pieces. Move on to the next stump until the job is done.

When I worked at the Resistor Plant in Boone, a farmer who worked for me on second shift told a story about his neighbor who decided to dynamite a very large oak stump close to his barn. Getting some bad advice from an in-law, the farmer wrapped tape around a dozen sticks of dynamite and put them under the stump. The dynamite blew the stump high into the air and the pieces came down on his barn roof, making several large holes. He also had a hole in the ground large enough to bury a mule. The concussion blew a hole in the side of his barn and knocked down his chicken house. He claimed that his dog wouldn't come out from under the porch, and his surviving hens wouldn't lay eggs for two weeks.

Incidents like the above notwithstanding, dynamiting stumps was a good method fifty to one hundred years ago, but not now. What with all the crime and terrorism, it's easier to get a date with Shania Twain than it is to buy a stick of dynamite. So it's back to the trackhoe.

When I was a kid, I used to walk around Nantahala with Dad and see all the beautiful pastures, fields and apple orchards. I can just imagine how long it took those venerable old pioneers to clear all that land. It was back-breaking work, but they did it, and I admire them for their dedication to their farms and families. I'm glad I didn't have to work as hard as my dad did. Grubbing one stump is one thing; grubbing an entire field is another. The plain truth is that most of us do what we have to do. At least if we're real men, we do.

Holed up by the Fire

The storm came up so suddenly that nobody expected it. It was Saturday night, and I had gotten permission to stay with Grandma Rosa and Uncle John, my step grandpa, but this was before the storm started. Our house was a quarter-mile up the road. The snow was two inches deep by the time Dad stepped up on the porch. "This is a wasted trip, son," he said, "but your mama wanted me to come down here and bring you home or tell you to stay put. Which do you want to do?"

I looked over at Grandma. "I'll stay if it's all right with you. I won't go outside, I promise."

Dad looked over at Uncle John. "I told Gladys that it would be a wasted trip, but you know how that woman is." He went out in the snow and headed back to the house.

He said later that the snow was six inches deep by the time he got home. It snowed about fourteen inches that night. The wind howled in the trees and sometimes the house shook. Uncle John had two thirds of the front porch covered in firewood and almost the entire back porch. There was also firewood under the porch and out in the shed. Clearly, we were not going to run out of wood.

Uncle John kept the fire going in both the kitchen cook stove and in the fireplace. When he wasn't lugging in firewood, he would sit and whittle on a stick. Every so often, he would reach over, pick up his whet rock, spit on it and sharpen his knife. When he was satisfied that it was sharp enough, he would shave a few hairs off his arm to test it. He made kindling by cutting into the stick until a wood sliver stood out in a half-moon shape, then another sliver until he had about a dozen. They made great fire starters in the morning. When he had finished with one stick, he would pick up another. His goal was to fill up the kindling box. That gave him something to do. I don't think it ever occurred to him to help Grandma with supper even though he had cooked in wood camps for many years. I never actually ate any of his cooking but Dad said it wasn't bad. Looking back, I think he meant that it wasn't all that good either.

After a while, I got tired of listening to the wind howl and watching Uncle John. I went in the kitchen to hang out with Grandma. She was just finishing up the cornbread. She greased her big skillet with a hunk of lard, top to bottom and all around. This was to keep the cornbread from sticking. Also, she kept her pan seasoned to perfection, and she would flog anyone who tried to wash it. After cooking, she wiped it with a clean cloth.

She had a big pot of pinto beans cooking in the fireplace. Naturally, they were seasoned with a side of fatback meat. I helped her slice the potatoes. She put those in another big skillet and began frying and browning. When she brought it all together, it was like manna from heaven. As always, I ate until I was about to pop. After we ate, she went back into the kitchen to clean up and Uncle John resumed adding kindling to the box.

When Grandma had finished, she came into the living room and joined us in front of the fireplace. She sat there for a few minutes, staring at the fire. Finally, she turned to Uncle John. "Why don't you tell the boy one of them yarns of yours, John?"

Uncle spit his plug of tobacco into his hand and threw it into the fireplace. He looked into the fire for a moment and began. "Way back when I was a boy," he said, "Uncle Henry Mason was always prowling around in the Nantahala Mountains looking for rubies and gold. One Saturday afternoon, he loaded a few provisions on his mule and headed out into the Tusquitees. Now, them mountains was wild in those days. There were bear, panthers and lots of rattlesnakes and copperheads. Uncle Henry's friends and family kept telling him that he was going to get lost or get mauled or bitten and disappear never to be seen again. Henry would just laugh and tell them he had to go sometime. His favorite time to hunt gold and rubies was November after the snakes and bears went into hibernation but before the big blizzards hit the mountains. Anyways, he headed out determined to find a Cherokee gold mine, even though he had already looked a thousand times. Certainly, nobody could fault him for giving up.

"On Sunday, it started snowing. It snowed all day, all night and all day the next. The wind howled and blew and nobody could see ten feet from where they stood. People would tie ropes from the house to the barn and sheds so they wouldn't get lost in the snow. It was that bad. Any livestock that wasn't in the barn died. When the storm finally quit on Tuesday, there was three feet of snow on the ground. Two weeks later, there was still a foot of snow and six feet drifts. Henry's wife and family decided there was no way he could still be alive. In their mind, he was buried and dead in the blizzard, never to be seen again. They held a funeral down at the church house, without Uncle Henry, of course. They even put up a grave marker at the cemetery.

"About six weeks after the blizzard, one of the grandkids looked down the road and saw Henry coming. She ran into the house to tell the others. At first, they thought the child was playing make believe. They all went out into the yard to look and sure enough, it was Henry. They all gathered around to ask him how it was that he was still alive. 'Well,' he said, 'I found a cave back under a big old rock overhang. Way back inside, the temperature wasn't that cold. Before long, I ran out of provisions and there was no way I could hunt. I slaughtered my mule and ate him. When the temperature started warming up, I packed snow around the carcass so it wouldn't go bad. One night, I had to shoot a panther off it. I would have eaten it if'n I had to, but I didn't. I'm telling you, it was a hard trip back without that mule.'

Later on, someone asked him if he ever found any gold. He would just grin and say, 'Well, I found a little bit, but I ain't never going back in them mountains again. I done learned my lesson.'"

Uncle John laughed. "Henry was getting old by then, so it was time to give up his prospecting anyway."

That night, I slept on a pallet in the living room so I could stay warm. Uncle John got up a half-dozen times to put wood on the fire. Sometime in the wee hours of the morning, Grandma came in and asked me if I was warm enough. I went back to sleep and dreamed about gold although I had never seen any except Uncle John's Double Eagle. Next morning, Dad slogged through the snow to check on us. He arrived just in time to eat one of Grandma's delicious breakfasts. And that's how life was in the Nantahala Community in the winter of 1948.

Mountain Heartbreak

There is nothing sadder than a tired, worried and depressed mother sitting by the bedside of a sick child, helpless and hopeless, unable to do anything except provide emotional comfort. The child coughs violently, her lungs rattle and she cries constantly, begs for relief but none is available. The mother hasn't slept for days, catching only a moment's nap as she sits in a straight back chair holding the child's hand. Her head hurts from stress, her muscles ache from lifting her daughter and she hasn't eaten in days. Her husband had died the year before, and she has six other children who are looking after themselves. The seventh died three week's ago and two more are coming down with the whooping cough. Neighbors have been kind, stopping by regularly and leaving food and other staples on the porch. They're afraid to come in the house for fear of contracting the disease and passing it to their own children.

The mother prays constantly and receives no answer for there is none. The nearest doctor is 75 miles away. Even if he could be brought to the home, he couldn't help for there is no cure, no vaccine, and no medicine that is effective against this dreadful disease. The mother knows that this child will be in the cemetery with the other one in a few days and more of the others may be also. Just a simple stone marker with no name inscribed on its surface will adorn the grave. In two generations, no one will remember which child is buried in which grave. The years will come and go and no one will record the suffering. All that remains is an old woman who survived the disease to feel the hurt in her heart as the years pass. She will take the pain to her grave, and the memories will be buried with her.

This is not fiction taken from Edgar Allen Poe; it is an accurate representation of the lives of many Appalachian men and women who survived to remember the thousands who died of those terrible diseases before modern science invented vaccines and antibiotics to eradicate the horror of watching helplessly as loved one suffered and died. Some of my old aunts, uncles and grandparents died with similar memories tucked away in secret corners of their minds. When asked, they would talk little, fearful of bringing the pain back to the surface.

We need simply to visit the old cemeteries and see the number of children's graves, often unmarked, and spread around in a haphazard fashion. Some of the stones that are marked will bring tears to our eyes as the notations are read. "Darling Child, Love of my Life, God's Special Gift" and other endearing terms that serve as remembrance to lives snuffed out too early by one or more of those old communicable diseases. No one knows how many really died from the ravages of those killers. Families were spread around the mountains in secluded hollows, hills and beside creeks and branches. They often buried their loved ones in small meadows, hillsides or even in the woods. Small church cemeteries were often neglected as descendants moved on to bigger churches. Sometimes nature took its course and covered them over with trees, bushes and vines. Decades later, a few conscientious people began to recognize the importance of those historical sites and began cleaning them up. Even so, thousands of unmarked graves will never be identified.

Back when my grandmothers were children, there were no doctors in Nantahala. It's that way today. Doctors who were available in larger towns such as Asheville and Knoxville were poorly trained, and more often than not, self-trained. This usually meant that they knew slightly more than their patients. Sometimes, they were even dangerous. The old grannies who had spent their lives practicing herbal medicine were often as effective as the nearest doctor, and sometimes more so. In those days, children were most often the victims of poor medical practice due to outbreaks of communicable disease such as diphtheria, whooping cough, small pox, polio, scarlet fever, measles, mumps and various strains of influenza.

While herbal medicines were often effective against such ailments as diarrhea, colds, sores, boils, pink eye, worms, lice and scabies, they were no match for most of the diseases. One either got well or one died; it was as simple as that. Too, people knew little about sanitary conditions, how the diseases were transmitted and how to protect against them. People ate from the same plates, shared food and drank from a common dipper. They went to church and sat next to others who were infected, sometimes with obvious symptoms, and yet, at that time, they were not recognized as such. People put their own lives at risk while caring for others and then mingled with friends and relatives, thus passing the diseases throughout the community.

By the time I was born in 1940, people began to understand the importance of simple cleanliness. Even though my family was poor, my mother used enough lye soap and bleach to kill half the diseases on the planet. Even so, she couldn't stop me from catching mumps, measles, scarlet fever and chicken pox from my schoolmates. I can still remember hallucinating as scarlet fever tried to consume my body. I saw monsters in the attic and had scary dreams and visions for days. Fortunately, my defenses overcame the disease and I lived to write about it.

Most of the old people have gone on to their reward and few people remain to tell about the sickness and death that walked these mountains. Like it or not, it's very much a part of our heritage and history. It's a fact that those who survived had better defensive systems and they passed those genes on to us. We are stronger people because of it, and we owe a debt of gratitude to those who died. Those unmarked graves serve as monuments to the children who never lived long enough to have families of their own. When I stand in the mountain cemeteries trying to make sense of the untimely deaths, I am reminded of the old preachers who often ended their eulogies with "The Lord giveth and the Lord taketh away; praise be the name of the Lord."

Ginseng and Molasses

My maternal Great-Grandfather, William Christenbury Mason, lived on Camp Branch about a mile above the Union Hill Baptist Church. He and Great Grandma Sarah Jane (Sally) were charter members. William was the Justice of the Peace for several years. He had a black car with a rumble seat which I think was a Model T Ford. In his later years, my Uncle Arthur drove him around in it. Prior to his death, he gave the car to my uncle. It sat at the edge of Grandma Rosa's yard when I was a kid. I don't know what finally happened to that car, but I guess Uncle Arthur sold it to somebody. I wish I could find it, but it probably ended up in a scrap yard somewhere.

Uncle Arthur loved to hunt ginseng. He would roam the Nantahala Mountains looking for it. He had a nose for 'sang' like a bloodhound has a nose for tracking people. I went with him on a few occasions, and I would hear him say, "There it is," and sure enough, he was right. He would dig it, carry the roots home in a sack or even in his pockets. He would lay them out to dry and then sell them to the first buyer he could find. I once went with him when he was 75 year'sold. He climbed the mountain behind Grandma's house like a bighorn sheep. It was all I could do to keep up with him, and I was 39 year's old at the time. Later, he had problems with his feet, probably gout, and he had to give up all that hiking and roaming around the mountains.

Uncle Arthur had a great sense of humor, and I loved to listen to him laugh at my dad's one-liners. He and Dad got along very well, and they would sometimes do things together. Dad got a lot of his jokes from my Great-Uncle John Owenby. I remember the three of them making sorghum molasses below the road in front of Grandma's house. I don't remember much about the cane mill, but I know they powered it with a horse or mule, depending on which one they owned at the time. A long pole was tied to a single tree which the horse pulled as it went round and round. The rollers would squeeze the juice out of the cane very much like the rollers on an old fashioned washing machine. They would cook the juice in a big pot somewhat like boiling clothes on wash day. They would keep a wood fire going under the pot until the juice reached the proper consistency, then pour it into a second pot and start boiling a fresh batch of juice. My Aunt Blanche sopped the boiler when she was a kid. Naturally, I took over her duties after she married and moved to Bryson City.

I would wait with eager anticipation until I could savor that sweet, delicious nectar of the gods.

Grandma and Mom would watch the fire and keep the cooking regulated. It took a good bit of skill to bring off quality sorghum.

They would get about one finished gallon of molasses for every six or seven gallon of juice. They stored buckets full of molasses in the cellar or in the barn. The women used it for sweetening most everything that we put sugar in today. Fresh blackberries sweetened with sorghum was one of my favorites. At that time, I had never tasted a store-bought dessert. I would let the juice run down my chin and then lick if off with my tongue. The fact that my chin might be dirty was of little consequence. Molasses cookies had a dark, musty taste that pleased the palate and warmed the soul. Of course, the syrup went real well with cathead biscuits and homemade butter. If one pulled a biscuit through a plate full of molasses and it didn't break, the molasses was just not made right.

Amos and Flossie Grant lived down below Grandma Rosa's house. They were a good Christian couple who raised thirteen children. As far as I know, all of them turned out to be model citizens. They had so many kids that visiting their house was almost like being at school. Of course, a couple of them were grown by the time the last ones came along. The amazing thing was that Amos and Flossie seemed to support their family as well as anyone else. Amos had a logging truck and he made his money by hauling logs to Nantahala to be loaded on the train. He also took people to doctors in Andrews or Franklin when it was necessary. He brought Elender Passmore to our house all three times to deliver my sister, brother and me. I don't know what Dad paid Amos, but I'm sure he did because that was his nature.

Dad had a long memory for debts he owed, and if he didn't have a way to pay at the time of a service, he would pay later even if it took years.

Amos usually didn't charge for helping people but Nantahala folk didn't want to be beholden to anybody so they would pay Amos as best they could. If they didn't have money, they would pay him with eggs, potatoes or anything else they had. Amos would take it because it took a lot of food to feed a family of fifteen.

Flossie was a good-hearted soul who would help anyone at anytime. She would sit up with the sick or help care for the dying. Where she found the time is beyond me, but she did. As my dad would say, "Amos and Flossie have gone on to glory," but they sure have a lot of descendents to remember them. Several of those thirteen kids had large families of their own.

After Dad died and Mom moved out of the house on Camp Branch, the Reverend Oscar Passmore would mow Mom's grass. He and Mom agreed on a price in the beginning and he never raised his rates. He charged about half of what anyone else would charge. Mom could never keep track of how much she owed him, and he would never ask her to pay. I would stop by his house occasionally and ask him how much she owed. He always knew the exact amount, and I would pay him.

Oscar came from a big family, and he and his wife, Blanche, raised a big family of their own. Oscar's grandfather and my great-grandfather were brothers. They were among the pioneers who settled in Nantahala after the Civil War. There are some older Nanta-hala memories documented by Weimer Cochran and maintained at Berea College in Kentucky.

Late to School

One fine day in spring, when I was in the third grade, I missed the school bus. We lived at the head of Camp Branch, and the school was on the upper end of Otter Creek, about six miles away, I think. I'm not sure why I decided to walk, but I did.

My Mom didn't know I missed the bus so I headed out. By that time, I had ridden the bus many times so I knew every curve in the road. Also, I had walked with my Dad to Weaver Cochran's store which was about halfway. I don't think it ever occurred to me that I might get lost. As I traveled, many things interested me along the way. It did then, and it does now.

I soon found that the walk was more interesting than when I went with Dad because I didn't have to hurry. The old adage about smelling the flowers along the way certainly applied in this case. By the time I reached the fork in the road where the Nantahala School is now, I had either looked at or touched everything of interest along Camp Branch Road. Obviously, I felt no reason to hurry.

At that point is where I decided to try a short cut. Instead of turning right toward Otter Creek, I turned left and went up the road toward Grandma Emma's house. Resisting the temptation for some of her delicious cookies, I slipped around through the woods because I figured she would tell Mom and Dad. I went up through her pasture to the top of the hill until I reached territory that was completely unfamiliar to me.

I headed down hill and after a few minutes, ended up in a laurel thicket. I worked my way around it and back up another ridge. After about three wrong turns, I decided to go back, but I couldn't figure out how to do that either. I don't remember being upset about it, but I may have been. I just kept trying to find my way out.

I headed down along a ridge until I came to a creek. I followed it downhill until I came to a pasture. I was about halfway across when the farmer's bull spotted me. He headed for me at a fast trot. I don't know if he intended to harm me or just thought I might have something for him to eat, but I wasn't taking any chances. I sprinted toward the other side of the pasture. I reached the barbed wire fence with some room to spare, but I knew I didn't have time to climb over, so I rolled under.

Murphy's Law always rules in these cases, so naturally, I rolled over a cow patty. But at least, I beat the bull. I walked down below the barn where the creek came around and washed the (grass and water) off my overalls. I don't remember the name of the people who owned this farm, but I think they were McMahans.

As I passed the house, Mrs. McMahan came out and called to me. I greeted her as casually as I knew how for an eight-year-old. Naturally, she asked me where I was going.

I told her to Otter Creek School. She asked if I knew the way. I told her I didn't.

"Come in the house," she said, "and I'll give you directions."

She also gave me a glass of cold buttermilk from the spring house and a big slice of cornbread with butter on it. Now, every kid should have a delicious snack like this for recess. A few minutes later, I left with a good set of directions.

I followed the farm road and came out on Briartown Road. I turned left as the lady had told me to do. In a few minutes, I came to Briartown Church; one of the landmarks she told me would indicate that I was going in the right direction.

Just above the church, I passed a house that was near the road. Those people had a mean looking dog that didn't like my presence. He took out after me. By now, the road ran uphill, and I headed out at a dead run. It only took a few seconds for me to realize the dog was going to catch me. I decided I was getting tired of running from animals. I stopped, picked up a big rock and turned. Luckily, the dog stopped also, and stood there snarling.

In those days, I was a champion rock thrower so I let him have it. The rock hit him on the head, and he ran down the hill howling as he went.

A woman at the next house up the hill saw the dog chasing me. She invited me in to wait just to make sure the dog wouldn't come back. She didn't ask me if I was hungry, she just brought out a big slice of sweetbread and a glass of milk. After eating, I started out again.

A little farther on, I topped the ridge, and I could see the school down the hill below me. In a few minutes, I came to the little country store just above the school.

I had a nickel in my pocket so I went in and bought five packs of kits. I walked slowly down the hill munching on the kits as I went. I arrived at the school during lunch. For some reason, I wasn't hungry so I didn't eat.

After the lunch period, I went to my room. My teacher, Mrs. Wilson, asked me where I had been. I told her I had missed the bus and walked to school.

That's a mighty long walk for an eight year-old boy," she said. "Did you have any problems?" she asked.

"No ma'am," I replied, feeling to make sure my overalls had dried.

I rode the bus home after school. I said nothing to my parents about my adventure. If anyone ever told them, I'm not aware of it. Of course, that kind of foolishness by a child is why I spent years worrying about my kids when they were away from home. I don't worry about my grandsons a lot. That's my son's job. What goes around comes around.

Sleeping Around

When I was a kid, I loved visiting other people. Most of the time, when I stayed away from home; it was at an uncle or aunt's house. I probably stayed at Uncle Voyd and Aunt Ruby's house more than anywhere else. After a delicious supper, we kids would do chores and if any time was left, we would play. At bedtime, I slept with two of my double first cousins, Kenneth and Darrell. I usually slept at the foot of the bed, between the two of them. If there was another visitor, like my cousin, Hoyte, four of us would sleep in the same bed, two at the head and two at the foot. As kids, we didn't really consider it a big deal, but I'm sure that four adults in a bed would drive them to distraction.

When we were eight or nine, we would cut up, laugh, and have a good time after we went to bed. Finally, Aunt Ruby would tell us to be quiet and go to sleep. She spoke with authority, and we did what she said. If they stayed at our house, we would usually ignore Mom, so Dad would order us to quiet down. Sometimes, we would stick our heads under the covers and whisper.

Back then, people usually took a bath on Saturday night, and in cold weather, it was behind the stove. Central heat did not exist in those days, at least not in Nantahala. Of course, Mom and my aunts were strong enforcers of the "hands, feet, face, neck and ears policy." Any kid who sneaked into bed without washing those body parts would get dragged out of the bed by his or her ears and forced to scrub said body parts with a rough cloth.

Because of this policy, sleeping at opposite ends of the bed was not a problem from an odor standpoint. When we were in a mood to cut up, we would stick our feet into the other's nose, and any other mischievous act that we could invent.

My Aunt Elva had a house full of kids, but by the time I started spending the night, the older kids had moved on, leaving four at home. Reva and Juanita were about my age, and Andy and Angie were younger. Andy and I slept in a room next to the kitchen and the women slept on the opposite side. I usually slept in a cot. I don't remember what kind of mattress it had, but it was comfortable. Even so, for some reason, I had bad dreams. I said nothing about it, because I loved to visit, and I didn't want to jeopardize my next visit. I spent the night there when I was in high school, and I had a dream about a train running over me. Apparently, I screamed out because I woke up with most of the family standing around the cot. At first, they thought I was just "cutting up," but they finally realized I was upset. Being the kindly saint that she was, Aunt Elva sent the others to bed, and she talked to me for a long time. I finally went back to sleep, and I guess she went back to her bedroom. I have never forgotten that.

My Uncle Arthur, Mom's brother, lived on Cartoogechaye for several years. I think we only visited them one time. Back then, it was a long way from Nantahala to Cartoogechaye. My cousin, Gerald, was quite a bit younger than me, but we still had a good time. We slept on pallets in a room near the creek. We cut up for a while until Uncle Arthur threatened to lock us up in the woodshed. Gerald went to sleep, and I lay quietly and listened to the babbling of the creek. I said that someday, I would have a house near a creek, but the nearest I ever got to one is where I live now, up the hill from Rose Creek. Next day, Uncle Arthur shot a big spider on the wall of his house. He dead-centered that spider, and of course, he put a hole in his living room wall. I don't know if he ever fixed it or not.

Staying at Aunt Lucy and Uncle Fred's house was a real trip. They had a big tribe also. All of her kids were older than me except Howard. I would try to follow the boys around but I was too young to keep up. I went ginseng hunting with Uncle Fred and a couple of the boys. Aunt Lucy was Dad's sister, and she certainly paid attention while Grandma Emma was cooking. I don't remember the name of it, but she made this stew that almost took my breath. I loved to eat it with big slices of cornbread and hot butter.

I had my own bed in the same room with Bobby.

Uncle Fred didn't put up with any nonsense so we were pretty quiet at night. We would whisper for a little while and then Bobby would stop for fear of getting a good thrashing.

I never stayed with Aunt Velma and Uncle Marshall until I moved to Valdese. They lived next door to us, so it really wasn't necessary to spend the night, but I did anyway. Aunt Velma would cook breakfast to order. I thought that was pretty cool. If I wanted my eggs over well, that's how she fixed them. As best as I can remember, she is the first aunt who ever fixed pancakes for me. I could have syrup or honey and plenty of hot, melted butter. Sometimes, she would put strawberries or blackberries on them.

I also stayed with a number of friends I got to know as I approached high school graduation. Randy Rhyne, a lifelong friend was my favorite non-relative. His mom and dad, Clyde and Pauline were super folks. They treated me like a son. Clyde helped me in the Boy Scouts and Pauline prepared many delicious meals for her family and me. On Saturday night, Randy, another friend, Harold, my cousin Hoyte and I would stay up and watch television. I never saw a TV the entire time I lived in Nantahala.

It goes without saying that I spent the night as often as I could with my Grandmothers. Both of them could have been gourmet cooks, but I doubt that either of them ever heard the word. Suffice it to say that either of them could take the simplest of meat and vegetables and turn them into mouth-watering meals. Back in those days, they didn't tell kids bedtime stories after they went to bed; they were told after the supper dishes were cleaned up or just before bedtime. I would often ask them to tell me about the outside world that I had never seen. I don't think either of them had ever been more than a hundred miles from home, if that far. Grandma Rosa would tell stories about Holland that she got from her grandmother. She told me about windmills and wooden shoes. When I actually went to Holland, that's the first thing I looked for. The windmills are a beautiful sight to behold, but wooden shoes are just plain uncomfortable. Maybe it's because my size thirteen English foot doesn't fit a Dutch shoe The Dutch eat a lot of crayfish (crawfish), but Grandmother considered them fish bait, I'm sure.

I'm surprised that my Mom and Dad didn't disown me as often as I stayed overnight elsewhere. In their waning years, they lived with my wife and me until Dad died. After that, Mom got her own apartment, and I stayed overnight with her from time-to-time. Maybe, I made up for all those nights I stayed away from home when I was a kid. I certainly hope so.

A Boy and His Dog

When I was twelve years old, a companion came into my life. Toby was a mixed breed dog, eggshell white with curly hair. He was a bundle of energy, and had the endurance of a greyhound. He could get a lot of mileage out of a leftover biscuit or a piece of fatback. In some ways, he looked like a poodle, but he was too bold and adventurous to be one. One spring morning, I found him under the porch. He was about half grown, not at all afraid, and he came to me when I called him. Because Dad didn't like animals around the house, I had never had a pet before. It took a lot of convincing before Dad agreed to let me keep him. He said that someone would probably show up to claim him, but no one ever did. None of the neighbors had ever seen him which led me to believe that he had been tossed out of a car in the middle of the night. Naturally, he wasn't allowed in the house. I named him Toby for no particular reason; that's just the first name that came to mind.

Before long, Toby became my shadow. Wherever I went, he went. When I came out of the house, I didn't have to whistle for him; he just appeared out of nowhere. If I rode my bicycle, I would ride at his speed so he could keep up. I didn't have to ride very slow because he could run like a coyote, although he didn't look like one. At first, he tried to follow me to school, but when I told him to go back, he reluctantly did so. When I came home, he would greet me by running in circles, jumping up and down and barking. He wouldn't quiet down until I petted him for a couple minutes. He was certainly a one-person dog. He kept his distance from everyone else.

If anyone came around the house at night, he would start barking and snarling. Dad liked that, so he decided that maybe Toby wasn't such a burden after all. Our neighbor, Ernest Powell, always kept a couple of dogs around. Toby wouldn't allow them or any other dog into our yard. He wasn't afraid to tackle a bigger dog if need be. He was quick and fast, and he could hold his own. Strangely, if the neighbor's dogs barked at night, Toby wouldn't join in like dogs are prone to do. He saved his barking and growling for people or dogs that came close to the house.

In the summertime, I would ride my bicycle to the creek which was about a mile away. Toby seemed to know where we were going, and he would be in the water before I got there. Sometimes, I would take a bar of soap and give him a bath. He loved the water, so it wasn't a problem. He would stand still while I soaped him down. When I finished, he would wash himself off by rolling and jumping in the creek.

I would find a deep place and sit in the water while Toby swam around in circles. He would bark when I splashed him, but he loved every minute of it. The water wasn't deep enough for me to swim in, so I would crawl along while he followed. Later, I would find a sand bank, lie in the sun and dry off. Toby would chase birds, rabbits, squirrels or any other creature that moved. Often, I would bring something to eat, and share it with him. He would sit patiently while I fed him one bite at a time. Afterwards, I would throw sticks, and he would bring them back. When we tired of that game, I would run through the meadows while he ran in circles, jumping and barking. He had boundless energy, and never seemed to tire.

When I was thirteen, Mom and Dad bought me a twenty-two rifle for Christmas. Mom really wasn't for the idea, but Dad said I was old enough to have one. He took me down in the woods behind Ernest Powell's house and gave me a couple of refresher lessons. He was an excellent shot, but that was the last time I ever saw him shoot a gun. Later, I would go rabbit hunting, and Toby would tag along. I taught him to bring the rabbits to me without chewing them up. He was quick to learn. He wasn't quite so good with doves. He would get too excited and scare them off before I could get into range.

At that age, I wasn't very good at shooting them on the fly. But then, I'd been taught that it wasn't sporting to shoot them on the ground. That's what I call the "Jerry Clower principle." Jerry said that when he was growing up, they only took three men and ten dogs coon hunting because they wanted to give the coon a sporting chance.

Later on, I became friends with Jimmy Greenway, a boy in my class at school. At first he lived on Main Street in Valdese. Later on, his mom married Troy Crouch, and they moved up on Crouch's Mountain. I would push my bicycle up there to visit and then ride it down the mountain as fast as I could go. Naturally, Toby went with me. Coming down the mountain, he couldn't keep up, so I would stop and wait for him at the bottom. In a few minutes, he would show up, tired but happy to see me waiting. This went on for about three summers.

One morning, I came out of the house, and Toby wasn't there to greet me. I whistled and called for him. No luck, so I started looking for him. It wasn't long before I realized that something bad had happened. I had this awful feeling down in the pit of my stomach. I looked all day, and just before dark, I found him lying behind some bushes. He was stone-cold dead, but I knew that the minute I saw his body. His stomach was bloated, and Dad said that someone poisoned him.

I took his body out in the woods where no one would know the location of his grave but me. For several days, I went off by myself and thought about the good times we had. I never talked about him to my friends. It was a personal matter that I had to work through by myself. I missed Toby for a long time. Sometimes I would go sit by his grave when I missed him badly. I never got another dog until after I married, and then I got one for the kids.

I still remember Toby with fondness. He gave

real meaning to the phrase, "man's best friend." He lived a short life, but he relished every minute of it. He was a perfect example of what love is all about; giving and not taking. Humans can learn a lot from dogs like Toby. If there's a dog's heaven somewhere; I'm sure he's there frolicking and having a good time.

Popcorn and Crackerjacks

One of my fondest memories is of the old Colonial Theatre in Valdese. Of course, it's gone now; a sad commentary on the good old days. We moved to Valdese when I was nine years old. I quickly started hanging out with my cousin, Hoyt Cooper, and two new friends, Randy Rhyne and Harold Whisnant. It wasn't long before they asked me to go to the movies with them. I asked my parents, and Mom steadfastly refused for several months.

"It's the devil's playground," she said. This was the same woman who, in her later years, would eagerly watch "Oh, Brother Where Art Thou?" three days in a row. Mom eventually gave in, and I went to the movies at age ten for the first time in my life. My favorite comic book character, Roy Rogers, starred in "The Golden Stallion." I was absolutely fascinated. At my next birthday, I asked for a set of Roy Roger's guns.

Another favorite cowboy was Gene Autry. The

first movie I saw starring Gene was "The Big Sombrero." I think that was the first color movie I had ever seen. Randy, Hoyt, Harold and I used to argue as to which was the better cowboy, Roy or Gene. We didn't realize that they were just a couple of well-paid actors. Both of them became rich men later in life.

Of course there was usually a cartoon and/or a serial every Saturday. The cartoons were typically Mickey Mouse, Donald Duck or Tom and Jerry. As a kid, I would wonder how they got all smashed up without getting killed. Of course, the serials were designed to keep kids coming back. Flash Gordon, Zorro, Buck Rogers, The Green Hornet and Captain Marvel would entertain us for ten or twelve weeks in a row. Naturally, we didn't want to miss a Saturday and lose out on another segment of a wonderful adventure. I especially remember that Flash Gordon's rocket ship looked like it had been made out of four or five sheets of roofing tin. When I looked close, I could see wires holding it up while smoke belched out the back end.

Unless our parents objected, we went to the matinee every Saturday. The cost was nine cents for kids under twelve and twelve cents for adults and kids over twelve. Popcorn and soft drinks were a nickel each. My favorite, Crackerjacks, was also a nickel. So, for nineteen cents, I could see a movie and have a drink with a snack. These days, the same thing will run at least ten dollars.

The old theatre probably looked like ten thousand others across America. The seats were wooden, well aged and carved by dozens of patrons. The floor was also aged with dirt, sodas and popcorn ground in.

Sometime later, I got a job cleaning up the theatre, and I actually got to see the place with the lights turned on. There was an old wooden stage with curtains that opened when the movie started. These days, they clean theatre floors with a leaf blower or some other modern device, but I had to use a broom. That took quite a while and I was making fifteen cents an hour. Between that job, my paper route and picking blackberries in the summer, I became financially independent, at least for recreational purposes. I always hated asking Dad for money and after age thirteen or so, I rarely did.

When we got a little older, we would try to find girls to go to the movies with us. The theatre had a balcony in front of the projection booth. Our first couple of dates would be downstairs where we would generally be limited to holding hands. If the wind was blowing in the right direction, we would invite the girl upstairs to the balcony. If the girl accepted, we would then proceed to the next step. The balcony was dark, more private than downstairs and a great place for a little smooching. The manager would pass through with a flashlight from time-to-time to make sure things were kept respectable. Of course, we could hear him coming by the time he hit the second step.

Later on, I got a job running the projectors. Now I was in the big time. The door to the projection room was kept locked to keep customers from wandering in. The flip side of this was that I could lock myself in with a girl. I remember one time in particular I got a little too interested in romance and let the film run out. As anyone who has been in a theatre remembers, whistling and cat calls begin immediately. I could hear the manager's footsteps coming up the stairs. I pulled the reel out of the projector and quickly mounted it in the splicing machine. He walked in and saw me bent over pretending to splice the film. "Hurry and get that reel spliced," he said, "We've got to keep the customers happy." As soon as he left, I grabbed the next reel and stuck it in the projector.

Another interesting event occurred when the film, "Singin' in the Rain," came to the theatre. After the last movie, the manager said that he would pay me overtime to run a particular reel for him. The reel was Cyd Charisse dancing in a sexy green dress. I can still remember the manager sitting in the middle of the theatre by himself while I ran that reel over and over. I must have run it a dozen times. In those days reels came in metal cases about ten inches in diameter. The reel and the case together probably weighed fifteen pounds. If it were the last movie, I would set the reels in front of the theatre for a truck to pick them up. They traveled from theatre to theatre. That time, the truck showed up and the driver had to wait until I got the manager's "favorite" reel loaded and out front.

Yes, the old theatre is gone now. The double doors that face Main Street are locked. Behind them is a hollow shell. The roof, the floors, the lobby, the projection booth and the stage are gone. Nothing is left but a patch of grass and weeds. I stood in the back where I guessed the lobby had been and looked out through the gaping hole in the brick wall. I closed my eyes and imagined The Lone Ranger galloping across the screen on Silver with the William Tell Overture playing in the background. Next came Allan Rocky Lane on Blackjack, Hopalong Cassidy on Topper and Red Ryder on Thunder. And of course, I couldn't forget Tonto on Scout, Little Beaver on Papoose and my favorite sidekick, Gabby Hayes.

I could hear happy kids walking up and down the aisles going for popcorn and crackerjacks. As I opened my eyes, it occurred to me that Mom was right; she was just fifty years ahead of her time. Most modern westerns aren't fit for kids to watch. When I walked back onto the street, I tried to remember the lyrics to the Statler Brothers' hit, "Whatever happened to Randolph Scott has happened to the best of me."

CHAPTER TWO
Uncles, Cousins, and Other Kin

Go South, Young Man

After my discharge from the Navy, I cooked at the Ribet Restaurant in Valdese, North Carolina, for a while. I found out later I wasn't the only family member who had cooked at one time or another. My great-great Uncle Clem was born in Pigeon Forge, Tennessee on April 22, 1847. By the time he was ten, he had a reputation for fouling things up. His five brothers entered the Civil War in 1861. Clem was only fourteen at the time so he had to stay home with his parents and his four sisters.

Being the only boy at home, he soon developed a love for wandering. Eventually, his dad gave up trying to break him of this habit and waited patiently until the boy came home. On his birthday in 1864, Clem decided to walk to Knoxville and investigate the sights and sounds of the big city. On his second night out, he went to sleep under a big walnut tree and was awakened by a squad of Union soldiers. Thinking fast, Clem told them that he was on his way to Chattanooga to join the Union Army. Before he could say Jumpin' Jehoshaphat, he was taken to a sergeant who enlisted him. Now, Clem was in a puddle of soup, but there was nothing he could do but play along. They issued him a rifle and gave him the usual three hours training.

Within a week, his regiment encountered a regiment of Confederate soldiers and a battle ensued. Not wanting to shoot his own people, Clem aimed his rifle at a rock and fired. The bullet bounced off and hit his second lieutenant in the leg. Suddenly Clem found himself without a weapon and a new assignment as the regimental cook. Unfortunately, he didn't know how to cook a bowl of grits, but it didn't matter because the Union guys didn't like grits and Clem knew nothing about tortellini and sauerbraten.

His regiment had now marched into rough country and there wasn't much food to be found. Clem was ordered to find something edible and make a big pot of stew. Since he didn't have a gun, the only thing he could run down was a family of possums. He promptly killed those with a stick and started looking around for some vegetables to mix with his meat. He found a tree loaded with green apples, some wild onions and a patch of mayapples. He put everything together in a big pot and lit up the fire.

His fellow soldiers, who were near starvation, thought Clem had made a great stew. Within an hour everyone came down with Montezuma's Revenge. Shortly, the entire regiment was out of commission because they couldn't march for stopping every ten minutes to visit the woods. Before the sun set, Clem's superiors had decided he was a Confederate spy.

In about three days, the regiment was again at full march. The advance scout told them a Confederate regiment was just beyond the next rise. The captain ordered Clem to lead the march thinking the young man would be the first to get shot. The scout had missed a group of Rebel soldiers hiding in the woods and Clem unknowingly led his regiment right past them. The Rebels decided not to shoot Clem because they didn't want to alert the marching soldiers behind him. After he passed, the hidden Rebels starting firing, and half his regiment was wiped out before the Confederates were driven away. The next day, his regimental commander called Clem into his tent, gave him a month's pay and an early discharge. "Go south, young man," the commander said. "Enlist in the Confederate Army and destroy it."

Hog Hunting on Gobbler's Knob

My Uncle Sarvis had an argument with my grandfather as to whom should inherit the south forty acres along the creek. Obviously, Uncle Sarvis wanted it. Grandpa wanted Aunt Matilda to have it so she could raise tobacco on it. She was an old maid who chewed three plugs a day so it seemed reasonable to the old man that she should have the acreage to grow her own.

Uncle Sarvis, as stubborn as Grandpa, packed up and moved to Gobbler's Knob in Mitchell County and never returned. One day, over a cup of home-made chicory, Dad suggested that I go visit his long-lost brother to see if I could find out how he was doing. It seemed like a strange request, especially since no family member had seen Uncle Sarvis in forty years and no one had seen any of his kids.

"Why me?" I asked Dad.

"Well son," he said, "You have a way with people

so they just might accept you."

I thought about that for a moment. "How do you know he won't shoot me?" I asked.

"No Owenby has every killed anyone except in self-defense," he replied.

"What about all those Yankees my Great-grandpa Porter shot in the Civil War?" I asked.

"Obviously, self-defense," Dad replied.

"Do you know where in Gobbler's Knob Uncle lives?" I asked Dad.

"Not exactly," Dad replied, "but you can bet your bippie everyone in that God-forsaken community knows exactly where he lives."

Next day, I headed out. It didn't take me long to get to Spruce Pine, but it took me longer to find some-one who knew where Gobbler's Knob was located. In desperation, I went to the police station and woke up the only cop on duty.

"Excuse me," I said, "but I'm trying to find Gob-bler's Knob."

He opened one eye and looked at me. "Now, why in the world would you want to go to that God-for-saken place?"

I wondered if he had been talking to Dad. "I've got an uncle who lives up there somewhere," I replied.

"Is he an outlaw or a moonshiner?" the deputy asked.

I told him Uncle's name. "I only know Sarvis be-cause his oldest son, Gray, is an outlaw. He's been in and out of jail a dozen times. I think the rest of his ten kids are okay though. Come on in here and I'll draw you a map."

I spent the night in Spruce Pine and headed out at dawn. I was glad I owned a four-wheel drive. The road up to Gobbler's Knob was like driving on the moon, except there were dense forests on both sides of the road. How Uncle found the place was beyond me. I took the deputy's advice and didn't stop at any houses until I pulled into Uncle's yard. I got out of my truck and walked up to the dilapidated porch. A woman and three girls sat in rickety chairs peeling apples.

"What chew want?" the woman asked.

"I'm looking for Sarvis," I said. "I'm his nephew."

She stared at me for a moment. "He's out back with the boys," she said. "Dey gettin' ready to hunt wild hogs."

I walked around the back and found an old man with a long beard. Three scraggly looking boys stood around waiting for directions. They all stared at me like I had broken into the hen house.

"Uncle Sarvis," I said quickly, "I'm your nephew."

Surprisingly, he smiled. "Ya gotta be Roy's boy. Ya look just like'em." He walked over and held out his hand. I took it.

"It's good to see ya, boy," he said. "Roy wuz my favoret brother. Is he still alive?"

"Fit as a fiddle," I said. Interestingly, the old man didn't ask about any other family members. I decided to let sleeping dogs lie.

"We're getting ready to kill us a hog," Sarvis said. "You wanna go with us"

"Sure," I said, realizing I had little choice. "How come you don't raise your own?" I asked.

"I hate hogs," he said. "But a man's gotta feed his family."

Sarvis introduced me to his boys. I was relieved that Gray wasn't one of them. The old man went into the house and came out with a rusty 12 gauge shotgun. He handed it to me. "It ain't much," he said, "but it'll shoot. Stay close to us and don't take no foolish chances."

It occurred to me that just going along was foolish. We headed up an old rutty logging road that wound around the side of Gobbler's Knob. Finally, Sarvis stopped and told us to be quiet. "I hear 'em," he said.

I heard nothing. We waited. Soon, I could hear them.

"Spread out," Sarvis said.

Suddenly, I was standing by myself. I quietly loaded the shotgun and sat down on an old stump to wait. I heard a noise, looked down and saw a piglet rooting around my feet. "Go away, you little devil," I whispered. "You want to get me killed?" I kicked at it gently.

Bad mistake. It squealed and almost instantly, I could hear a racket. I looked up the hill and saw a boar about the size of a freight train running toward me at a rapid pace. It looked like a rhino with tusks. I jumped up and started running along the trail with the huge boar right on my heels. I twisted around, shot and missed. I threw the shotgun down and grabbed a big hickory limb that hung about seven feet above the ground. I swung up like a monkey. The freight train roared past right under me.

I looked toward the washed out logging road and saw Sarvis standing in the middle of it. As the boar rushed him, he never moved. I heard a boom and the hog went down. It lay dead about two feet from Sarvis' feet. I climbed down out of the tree. The three boys came out of the woods from somewhere. We all stood looking at the biggest boar I had ever seen. The youngest boy, Lem, was the first to speak.

"Ain't daddy sumpin'?" he declared. "He's got more nerve than a rottin' tooth."

I looked at the hog and then looked at Sarvis. "How're you going to get that thing to the house?" I asked.

"Boys," the old man said, "go git the mule and the sled. Me and Roy'll stay here and talk 'til ya git back."

While we waited, the old man caught me up on his life. He had no regrets. When the boys returned, we pushed and shoved until we got the hog on the sled. Lem led the mule and the rest of us followed.

Apparently, Lem had told the women that the hunt had succeeded. They had two big tubs of scalding water waiting when we arrived. The old man hooked a winch to the hog's hind legs and the boys pulled it up. In less than an hour, they had the hair removed with the scalding water. Sarvis dressed the hog out like an expert.

I stayed for three days and enjoyed some fine country cooking. As I prepared to leave, Sarvis walked me to the truck and shook my hand again. "Come back anytime," he said.

"You come see us," I replied.

"I don't 'spect I'll ever leave this mountain," he replied, "but thanks."

Back home, I went to visit Dad.

"Well, how'd it go son?" he asked.

"Sarvis sends his love," I answered.

Dad grinned. "Bout time," he said.

The Best Cook in the Family Tree

One Saturday afternoon, Dad and I were talking about our family tree. He asked me why I hadn't stopped off in Pickshin, West Virginia, to visit his cousin, Grundy, on one of my walkabouts.

"I didn't know you had a cousin named Grundy," I said.

"Yes, I do," Dad informed me. "Old Grundy is my half-sister's first cousin on her mama's side."

I did the math in my head before asking the next question. "Is Grundy his first name or last name?"

"Last," Dad replied. "His first name is Monday."

I mulled that one over. "Was he born on Monday?" I asked curiously.

"Nobody knows," Dad replied. "He was born so far back in the hills his family didn't know what day of the month it was, let alone the day of the week. Nobody knows how old he is, but I guess he'll live till he dies."

I waited patiently for Dad to continue his story. There was no one present but us, but still, he whispered. "It's kind of a family secret that ol' Grundy has a still up on Devil's Backbone north of his house. The revenuers have hunted it for years with no luck."

"So Grundy's never been caught," I speculated.

"Well, he sold a pint to an undercover agent once," Dad answered. "But his court-appointed lawyer got him off."

"How did he manage that?" I asked.

"The lawyer put Grundy on the stand, and then he walked over to the jury box." "Ladies and gentlemen of the jury," he said. "Take a good look at this man. If he had any whiskey, do you think he would sell it?" Dad gave one of his little chuckles. "They acquitted him. Probably half the jury had bought shine from Grundy at one time or another."

On my next walkabout, I stopped off in Fleatown, Ohio, to visit an old Navy buddy. On the way back, I remembered my promise to pass through Pickshin to visit Grundy. I figured I had a choice of two routes, neither of them good. In Odd, West Virginia, I came upon an old man sitting in a cane chair in front of a deserted filling station. Thinking I might spook him, I stopped about fifty yards beyond the station and walked back. "Lived here all your life?" I asked.

"Not yet," he replied. I laughed at his quick wit and then asked him the best way to get to Pickshin.

He gave me a big, toothless grin. "I bin sittin' here in this chair for nigh on to twenty years; ain't nobody ever axed me how to get to Pickshin before. Ain't nobody lives up there but the Swiltons and the Grundys, and you don't look ugly 'nuff to be one of them."

"I'm afraid so," I said. "Monday Grundy is my cousin twice removed on my half-aunt's side."

He leaned over in his chair and spit tobacco juice into an empty tomato can. "If ye kin keep up with all that, I reckon I can help ye some," he ventured.

"Grundy raises hogs," the old man told me. "And so did his pappy and his grandpappy. Hogs have been in that family so long that it's hard to tell a Grundy from a Yorkshire. Grundy's got a still way back in one of them hollars. Law don't bother him 'bout it. I suppose they gave up years ago. They used dogs, copters and a whole passel of men and never found nothing." He leaned over and spat in his tomato can again. "Now, if yer still intent on sufferin', I'll tell ye how to find Grundy."

He pointed to a road that went up a steep hill. "Might as well put yer gears in bulldog, cause it's a hard pull. When the macadam quits, thar'll be three forks. Take the one on the left. If'n ye take the one on the right, God help ye. Them Swiltons don't like strangers. After 'bout a mile, ye'll come to an old gristmill that's been shet up for years. Unless you've got one of them four-wheel drives, park yer car there. Walk up the hill and when ye top the gap, ye'll see Grundy's place. It's hard to tell hit from the hog pens on the outside, but Grundy's better half keeps it spiffy on the inside. If'n hit twarn't for her; old Grundy wouldn't take a bath but onct a year. She even makes him warsh his feet when he comes in from the hog pens. Don't blame her none. Them Yorkshires smell to high heaven."

The old man was right. Grundy's place smelled worse than a locker room full of Frenchmen after a soccer game. A barefoot boy wearing overalls and nothing else met me halfway down the hill.

"I'm not the law," I said to put him at ease.

"I knows that," the boy said. "Ya don't smell like one so who are ya?"

"I'm your cousin, son," I said.

He stared at me for a moment. "Ya don't favor paw none."

"Thank you," I said. "Is Grundy about?"

"He's out back with the dogs," the boy said. I held my breath as I passed the hog pens. I made it around the corner of the house before I had to breathe in. I found Grundy feeding table scraps to a pack of hounds.

"Down Razor, down Roscoe," he admonished them as he tried to feed the others.

Grundy looked up just as I approached. "You shore look like your daddy," he said.

"You look like yours, too," I replied.

"My bad luck," he chuckled. We made small talk for a few minutes. It occurred to me that Grundy didn't know how to make big talk. After a bit, he suggested that we go in the house. "Cora Lee's probably got supper ready by now."

"She may not be expecting a guest," I said.

"She knows yer here," Grundy said. "Tain't nothing 'scapes her."

Once inside, Cora made us wash our hands just like all country mothers do. She had prepared pork chops, polk salad, taters and cornbread.

"Them pork chops shore are good, Cora," Grundy said. "Where'd ya git'em?"

"Well, duh, Grundy," Cora said. "If'n ya'd counted yer hogs lately, ya'd know."

"I don't 'member no killin'," he declared.

"Ya probly don't," Cora replied. "Ya stay in the woods all the time up at ya know where, cooking ya know what."

Grundy rolled his eyes in my direction.

"Your secret's safe with me," I said.

"I know yer dad can keep a secret," Grundy replied. "I suppose ya can, too. If'n hit's foggy in the morning, we'll go cooking.

"Fine with me," I replied. "I'll try anything twice."

Next morning I awoke to Cora's voice calling Grundy, their kids and me to breakfast. We all sat down on the benches next to the table. The oldest girl asked the blessing. It wasn't hard to tell that Grundy raised hogs. A big platter in the middle of the table held sausage, bacon, country ham and well-done eggs. Cathead biscuits and sawmill gravy made their way around the table. Cora beamed when I filled my plate for the third time. All country mothers can tell how much their cooking is appreciated by the amount of food that is eaten.

After breakfast, Grundy and I stepped outside to be greeted by the thickest fog I had ever seen. We felt our way out to the rickety old barn. Grundy hitched his mule up to a wagon that stood by the barn door.

"You don't have a car?" I asked, showing my ignorance.

"Yeah, I got a Ford pickup out thar in the shed," he said. "But it won't go where we're goin'."

After about an hour's climb, I found out that the wagon wouldn't go where we were going either. I helped Grundy pack the sugar and corn across a mule's back. "Ain't no way I could find my still in this fog," Grundy said, "but old Bess can. That mule could find a Methodist in a church full of Baptists."

Continuing on up the mountain, we stopped three times for about fifteen minutes. "We must be very quiet," Grundy said.

We couldn't see anything in the fog, of course, but he listened intently. I knew he was making sure no one followed us. We went through some laurel thickets that I was sure an elephant couldn't manage, but that old mule just kept on going.

We came up on his still so suddenly that I didn't know we had arrived. We had come through a narrow opening between two cliffs and the still was under an overhang. A small stream poured out through an opening in the rock, dropped down into a crystal-clear pool and then disappeared underground. Now I understood why the law never found Grundy's still. It couldn't be seen from the air and one had to be standing on top of it to see it from the ground. In the past, the revenuers had probably followed the stream uphill and concluded that it ended where it came out of the ground down below us. They might have been within a hundred feet of the still and never knew it.

We unloaded the toe sacks of corn and bags of sugar that we brought with us and put them in a big metal box with a lid that felt like it weighed a ton. I couldn't help but wonder how Grundy had gotten it there. Instead, I asked him how he obtained all that sugar without arousing suspicion.

"I have an old Army buddy that works in a sugar processing plant in Findlay, Ohio," Grundy said. "He brings down a truckload of sugar when I need it. On the side of his truck is a big sign that says, Ohio's Best Hog Feed. I pay him with gallons of my best Panther Breath. He drives back home, pours them gallons into pints and makes some extra money."

Grundy had a long plastic pipe that he used to divert the little stream into a big iron tub. Despite the dampness from the fog, we got the fire started. When Grundy was satisfied, he piped the hot water over the corn, added sugar, yeast and a small amount of his secret herbal ingredients. Nobody knew his ingredients, not even his wife. Next, we moved to a 55 gallon barrel and began processing the corn by removing the sprouts and roots.

I asked him why he didn't use cornmeal. "Hit don't taste right," he said.

Next, we poured the corn into a third barrel and mashed the mush with a special wooden tool that Grundy had made. We set it aside to ferment next to three others already in process. Then, he selected one of the barrels that had fermented to his satisfaction, and we prepared to cook the contents.

We strained the ingredients through a fresh pillow case that Grundy had brought along for that purpose. This filtered out the solids before we started cooking. I had the enviable task of starting the fire.

When the clear liquid began dripping from the copper pipe, he invited me to taste it.

"I don't drink it, Grundy," I said, "but I've sampled quite a few batches in my time." I had to admit it was the smoothest flavor I'd ever tasted. When we had collected ten gallons, we packed them on his mule.

On the way down, I asked him if he only cooked on foggy days. "Always," he replied. "Last year, we had ninety-nine foggy days. That's enough to keep my supply goin' and nobody can see my smoke."

Back at the farm, Grundy left me with Cora while he went to hide his day's production. I felt a little put off because he didn't want me to know his hiding place, but Cora told me that she didn't know where he stored it either.

"I've looked all over this farm and I can't find it," she chuckled. "Six revenuers came with a search warrant and looked all day and they never found it."

While we waited on Grundy, she told me he never sold to anyone but his regular customers despite the fact that a lot of people came around asking. "He loses bizness that way, but ya never know who's the law and who ain't."

The day after I returned from my trip, I drove over to see Dad.

"Did you stop off and see Grundy?" he asked.

"I did," I said. I told him about being Grundy's assistant for a day.

He laughed. "You're probably the last generation to ever see a still in action. I suppose Grundy told you about the trick his nephews tried to pull."

I thought for a moment. "I don't think so," I said.

"Well," he began, "everyone knows that Grundy makes the best moonshine in West Virginia. Even Popcorn Sutton couldn't do better. Anyway," Dad continued, "Grundy's nephews, Riley and Homer, decided to compete with him, but their shine tasted little better than kerosene. They came up with the brilliant idea to duplicate Grundy's shine. Somebody told them that the department of agriculture would analyze any farm product sent to them and return a report.

"They asked Grundy for a pint of his best. When their sister told on the boys, Grundy decided to pull a trick of his own. He kept watch until they put their sample in the mailbox. After they walked back to the house, he sneaked their sample out of the box and replaced it with his own sample. In about three weeks, the boys received a report from Charleston.

"Dear Sirs," the letter said, "As requested, we have analyzed your sample and the results are enclosed. Your sample contains urea, chloride, sodium, creatinine and a long list of enzymes which can be provided upon request. The test also revealed that your animal's sugar level is twice as high as it should be. In other words, your mule has diabetes. We recommend that you take him to the County veterinarian post-haste. Sincerely, Baxter Griswald, Chemical Specialist."

Dad laughed long and hard. "Did the nephews ever figure it out?" I asked.

"Are you kidding?" he replied. "Grundy's mule is smarter than those two."

"Did he take his mule to the vet?" I persisted.

"Yes, he did," Dad said. "The vet couldn't find anything wrong. A few days later, Grundy figured out the problem by himself. While he cooked his mash, old Bess had been snitching sugar out of the bags behind his back."

The Snipe Hunt

As I dressed to go into town, the phone rang. I hesitated to answer it, but, like most people, my curiosity got the best of me.

"How's thangs in the flatlands, cuz?" the voice said.

I searched my memory, trying to recall the speaker's identity. Momentarily, a light bulb came on. "How's it going, Zeke?" I asked.

"Dang, I told Zeb you'd know who it wuz." A moments silence and I heard him yell into the background, "Y'owe me a beer Zeb," and then a loud snicker.

"How are things in Turkey Ford, Zeke?" I asked.

"Purty good, Cuz," he replied. "We sold twenty gallons to our buyer in Red Bush last week. Now, we got us a wad of dead Presidents to see us through fer a while."

"You guys are going to get caught one of these days," I advised.

"Maybe," he replied, "but there ain't no other way to make any foldin' stuff around this neck of the woods."

We chatted a while longer. Zeke was a good source for catching up on Uncle Riley's side of the family. Finally, I asked him why he was calling.

"Well, Cuz," he said, "me and Zeb got to talkin'. You ain't bin up here fer a while so we thought we would give you an invite fer a snipe hunt."

I heard Zeb snickering in the background.

"Is this a serious offer, Zeke?" I asked. I'm thinking, surely he doesn't believe I'm dumb enough to fall for that old ruse. And then it dawned on me, maybe he does. After all, Zeke and Zeb weren't the brightest bulbs on the family chandelier.

"Yeah, cuz," he replied. "We wuz thinkin' maybe Saturday."

"Could I come up Sunday instead?" I asked.

"Okey dokey," he replied. "Can you git here in time to sample Maw's cookin'?"

My mouth watered when I thought about Effie's cornbread and fried potatoes. "I'll be there in time, Zeke," I told him.

"Good," he said, "I'll tell her to put out an extra plate. Then after dark, we can go see if we can catch us a nice fat snipe."

I decided to play along. "You mean that you can only catch them at night?" I asked.

"Yeah, cuz," he replied. "They sleep in the day-time so there ain't no use lookin' for'em until they wake up."

"I understand," I said. "Lookin' forward to it."

After I went to bed, I stared at the ceiling and tried to think of a way to give Zeke and Zeb a taste of their own medicine.

On the way to Turkey Ford, I stopped off at a friend's house. I knew he raised ferrets, so I asked him if he would sell one.

"I'll give you a dozen if you want," he said. When I told him what I wanted it for, he gave me a two-year-old female. "They're not as rambunctious as males," he said, "so she will make it easier to pull off your surprise."

I put the ferret in a cloth bag so it could breathe and then concealed it in the back of my truck. Back on the road, I realized I was running late so I picked up the pace with no stops. I didn't want to be late for supper because I knew from experience that Effie was the best cook in Surry County.

I arrived a few minutes early which gave me some time to jaw with Zeke and Zeb. Riley had died two years ago and the boys had moved in with Effie so they could look after her. The real truth was probably the reverse. They were a pair of natural born comedians and practical jokers who didn't take life seriously.

Effie came out on the porch and called us to supper. The food was worth the trip. Effie's hominy and cornbread were to die for. Even though it was late November, she had canned everything a garden can produce and cooked it to perfection. The fried chicken was so crunchy that Colonel Sanders would have eaten his heart out.

Half an hour later, I pushed away from the table, sated and satisfied. I offered to help with the dishes, but Effie declined, saying that she wanted me to go out and enjoy the boys.

Enjoying those two consisted of watching them milk two cows and a goat. It took both Zeke and me to hold the goat while Zeb extracted the milk. Next, we took some hay out of the barn loft and fed two mules that Zeke said were 32 years old. While they slopped the pigs, I sneaked over to my truck and stuck the ferret under my coat. It wiggled a little bit and then settled down.

At dusk, we jumped into Zeke's old truck and headed out for snipe territory; at least that's what Zeb said. After driving on a dirt road for a couple of miles, we stopped at the foot of a gulley. Zeke pulled a toe sack out of the back of his truck and handed it to me. He cut down two small saplings and chopped them into five-foot lengths. He said that he and Zeb would use them to drive the snipe downhill. Once they were ready, we walked up the gulley some fifty feet and stopped.

Zeke gave a demonstration on how to hold the bag just so. He said that snipes were very fast and he didn't want me to miss it. When he was satisfied that I understood his instructions, they headed on up the gulley. They would beat the bushes with their sticks and run the snipe down to me. I could hear them snickering and giggling as they walked up the hill. Before long, I heard them whacking tree trunks and limbs.

Then suddenly Zeb called out, "Get ready, here comes the snipe."

I pulled the ferret out from under my coat and

quickly transferred it to Zeke's sack.

Shortly, I could hear Zeke and Zeb working their way downhill through the bushes. In a couple of minutes, they were standing in front of me holding a flashlight.

"Did you catch the snipe?" Zeke asked. I thought Zeb was going to pop a button off his shirt.

"I sure did," I replied. As I started walking toward the truck, I saw them give each other a puzzled look. I leaned my back against the truck and held up the sack. "Sure is a lively one," I said as the ferret jumped around in the sack.

"What'cha got in that sack, cuz?" Zeb asked.

"I reckon it's the snipe," I said. "It ran into the sack while you boys were making all that racket."

They kept glancing at each other when they thought I wasn't looking. "Can I see it?" Zeb asked.

"Sure," I replied, "but don't let it get out."

Zeb eased the string off the bag and stared down into it while Zeke shined the light.

Zeke couldn't see it, and he was getting anxious. "What is it, Zeb?"

"Durned if I know," Zeb replied. "I ain't never seen nothin' like it."

Zeke walked around to the driver's side and turned on the headlights. Zeb carried the bag into the light. They both looked down into the bag and began whispering which I could easily hear.

"I think it's one of them minks," Zeb said.

"I think yur right," Zeke said. "That thing's probably worth a hundred bucks."

"Shh," Zeb said. "He'll hear you."

They closed the bag and walked over to me.

"Kin we have it?" Zeke asked. I hesitated for a moment. "Give you five bucks for it," Zeb said quickly. "Okay," I replied, trying not to appear easy.

Back at the house, they went in to show their prize to Effie. They all came out on the porch.

"Guess I'd better head out," I said. Effie tried to get me to stay.

"The boys are going back to dry gulley tomorrow to see if they can find any more minks. I'm sure they could use your company."

"I'd love to," I replied, "but I've got a job interview in Mount Airy in the morning at 11:00. I have a motel reservation at the Mayberry Motor Inn."

I gave her a hug and then climbed into my truck. As I turned around and headed down the road, Zeke called out, "Say hi to Andy and Aunt Bee for me."

Uncle Alf and Aunt Theo

My Great-Great-Great Uncle Mortimer Fenley intended to name his sixth child and third son; Theodore. In those days, children were delivered by midwives and Theodore was brought into the world by Aunt Matilda Mashburn who was getting on in years. As it were, Matilda had just delivered another baby, a girl, about two hours earlier. Apparently, she mixed up the girl's and Theodore's names when she turned them into the county record keeper.

A few weeks later, Uncle Mort received a birth certificate and Theodore turned out to be Alice Louise. Now, Uncle knew that Theodore would be unmercifully teased with a girl's name. So, from about the time he was six months old, his parents called him by his initials; ALF or Alf. Now Uncle Mort and Aunt Rachel kept the secret except for one thing. They duly recorded Alf's name in the family Bible to be Alice Louise. Of course, the girl down the road who was supposed to be Alice Louise was named Theodore and her parents called her Theo.

Now, everything went well until Alf was about twelve years old. One day, his older brother, Thomas, got to nosing around in the family Bible and discovered Alf's secret. As everyone knows, siblings can be unmerciful with their teasing. Thomas spread the word rapidly and in a few days, Alf's brothers and sisters were giving him a hard time.

It didn't take long for Alf to get fed up. Soon, he was devising methods of getting even. For starters, he hit Thomas in the head with a rock which addled his older brother and caused substantial bleeding. After Alf got a hard whipping for that, he decided he had to be more subtle with his moments of revenge. When an older sister, Velma, began teasing him, he quietly put horse manure in her bathwater. Of course, she told on him but he claimed he had been in the barn at the time and couldn't possibly be the guilty party. When he escaped a whipping for that one, he began to conjure up other methods that would insure freedom from punishment.

As it turned out, Thomas told one of his buddies in school and word spread like wildfire. He got a resounding whipping for that but it was too late. A couple weeks later, Alf and Theo managed to figure out what had happened. From that day on, they became partners-in-crime; or to put it a better way, how to get even without getting punished. There was one boy in particular, the school bully naturally, who turned up the heat on the two wrong-named kids. Part of the reason he was so uppity was because his parents were a little better off financially than most of the other families. He began to ridicule Alf and Theo unmercifully. Before long, he started having problems of his own. He rode a horse to school every day so the two plotters put a chinquapin under his saddle just before he started home. He made it about fifty yards before the horse threw him off resulting in a knot on his head, two sprained wrists and a serious blow to his pride.

Alf and Theo decided to spy on the bully after school to see if they could come up with some fresh ideas. They soon discovered that he had a secret swimming hole where he went skinny dipping on hot afternoons. They sneaked up to the bushes where he hid his clothes and tossed them in the river downstream. Meanwhile, they had invited the entire school to watch. Bully came out of the water naked as a jaybird and went to get his clothes, which, of course, were missing. As he stood there scratching his head, about thirty people came out and started laughing.

To add insult to injury, Theo spread the word that he was deficient in some parts of his anatomy. After that, Bully didn't come to school for two weeks. When he finally returned, Theo and Alf told him his troubles were just beginning if he continued to ridicule them. He got the message and promised to beat up anybody else who ridiculed them if they would leave him alone. They agreed.

As the years passed, Alf and Theo became inseparable and at age seventeen, they married. Three months later, the Civil War broke out and Alf found himself in the sixth Georgia Cavalry.

For two years, Theo sat at home and worried and

prayed. Then one spring morning, Alf came walking up the road with his arm in a sling. He had been shot in the shoulder, but he didn't have permanent damage. He also found that he had a twenty month old daughter he had never seen. Theo had been patiently waiting for Alf to get home so they could name her. After considerable discussion, they decided to give her a name that no one would ridicule. They named her Alex which could be a boy's name or a girl's name.

Alf had saved every penny of his meager military pay so they moved to North Carolina, bought some land and built a house and barn. Soon they were blessed with a boy and they named him Jamie. The next eight were named Ashley, River, Bay, Logan, Chris, Kelly, Taylor and Frankie. Anyone who heard the name of one of the children but had never seen him or her would have to ask the gender of the child.

Now Ashley was my great-uncle and he often told this story to his children, nephews and nieces, grandchildren, grandnephews and grandnieces as he sat by the fireplace smoking his corncob pipe.

Whether the story is true or not, I couldn't say. Grandma told me that Uncle Ashley had exaggerated a time or two, but in those days, stories were told just as much for entertainment as for historical accuracy.

Way Out on a Limb

I was talking to my cousin, Elwood, the other day. Elwood is my fifth cousin, twice removed. Try explaining that to a ten-year-old. Anyway, Elwood has a part-time job parking cars at the Peach Leaf Gentlemen's Club in Bluefield, West Virginia.

Now, before you ask, that's not where I ran into Elwood. I actually ran into him at the Walnut Springs Hog Farm and Co-op in Rocky Gap. Elwood's family moved to that area when he was six-years-old. His dad, Cletus, told me at the family reunion on Stillhouse Branch that he considered leaving Elwood in the empty house on Needmore Road, but he wanted the boy to get one of them fancy West Virginia educations. Elwood tells people that he finished sixth grade but I know for a fact that he dropped out in the fourth. His mother, Velma Jane, told me that the other boys ridiculed him because he had all his teeth.

Elwood had walked over from the hog farm to get

himself, to use his words, a sodi-water. I won't say what his job at the farm involves, but he had on tall rubber boots and carried a shovel. He also had on overalls and no shirt. I've seen gorillas with less hair. I figured he got that from his mama's side of the family. I might not have noticed him if the other customers hadn't crinkled their nose and moved several feet away. I greeted him warmly, but kept my distance.

"Hi Elwood, how's tricks?" I asked.

He gave me an angry stare. "You asking about my other job?" he said.

"I'm your cousin, Roy," I said. "Remember?"

"Sorry," he said. "I thought you wuz one of them smart alecks from over Bluefield way. How you been, cousin?"

"Doing well, Elwood," I said. "How's Blumadene?"

"She's gained a little weight," he said, "but totherwise, she's fine."

"I never have figured out how you married such a pretty woman," I said. "You must be quite a talker."

"Naw," he said, "I just put on a shirt and wore clean overalls."

You sure got over that, I thought, but I kept my opinion to myself. "You got kids now?" I asked.

"Shore do," he said, "two of'em. I've taught'em to hunt and fish and last Saturday, they went coon huntin' by theirselves."

"What's their names?" I asked. "Shirline and Trixibelle," he said proudly.

"They're girls then," I said.

"Yup, shore are," he said. "They're purty as a picture, bof'em."

"They must have gotten that from Blumadene," I ventured.

"I reckon," he said, "but they weigh a whole lot less." He laughed at his own joke.

"You make it sound like she's fat," I said.

"Not as bad as she wuz," he said. "She's down to 250 now."

"Wow," I said. "The last time I saw her, she wouldn't have weighed more than 95 pounds soaking wet."

"It's all that fatback, biscuits and gravy and possum grease," he said. "When I wuz sparkin' her, all she et wuz carrots and lettuce. The day after we started keepin' house, she came home with a buggy load of ham hocks, livermush, souse meat and chicken gizzards."

I grinned. "Pulled the wool over your eyes, did she?"

"Sumpn' like that," he said.

"How are Cletus and Velma Jane?" I asked.

"Ma's finer than frog hair," he said. "She went to one of them fancy beauty schools over Green Valley way. She made a mess out of Blumadene's hair though. When she got done, Bloomie looked like she'd been scared by a haint. I told the girls to run like the dickens if she came near them. Pa ain't too happy though. They caught him over by Pine Top with a load of shine. He told them it wuz for medicinal purposes, but they didn't buy it. Turned out, the sheriff owed him a favor for keepin' his mouth shut, so they let him out of jail after two weeks. Ennyway, you know Pa. He felt like it sullied his reputation."

What reputation, I thought. He's been making and hauling the stuff for forty years. Curiosity got the best of me so I asked Elwood what favor the sheriff owed Cletus.

"Pa wuz out deer huntin' one day and came up on Sheriff Shatys backed up in one of them hollers with the motor running. Pa thunk sumpin might be wrong so he ambled down to the truck to check. Sheriff and the widder Tewey wuz all hugged up in the front seat."

"So what happened?" I asked. "Well Pa said that Shatys got all mad about it, but the widder woman just smiled and said, 'Hello, Cletus.'"

"Wonder why the widow was so friendly," I mused. Elwood laughed.

"She oughta been. Her daughter, Hickie Sue, is my half-sister."

"So that means that Hickie Sue is my half-fifth cousin, twice removed." I said.

"Durned if I know," Elwood replied. "I can't count that high."

"Anywhere around here I can get something decent to eat?" I asked Elwood.

"Shore," he said. "Which way's yore machine faced?"

"I'm headed south," I said.

"There's Skeeter's Restaurant over in Harts," he said. "Ma works there. She can fix you as good a plate of vittles as you've ever tasted."

"I thought you said she was a beautician."

"She is," he replied. "She cuts hair in the back when bizness is slow."

"I hope she doesn't do both at the same time," I said. Elwood looked blank for a moment. "Just kidding, Elwood," I said.

"You could wait till I get off work," he said. "You can go home with me. Blumadene's making pork pot pie tonight."

"I thought you said she was on a diet." "She is," Elwood replied. "She'll sit at the table and eat carrots and lettuce. After I finish eatin' and go out on the porch, she'll sneak the leftovers."

"That's my idea of a good diet," I said.

"I really do appreciate the offer, Elwood, but I guess I'd better take a rain check."

"Don't take no wooden nickels, cuz," he said.

I watched his back as he headed toward the hog pens. He had slung his shovel across his shoulder, and I could hear him whistle while he walked. I was reminded of a quote by Ralph Waldo Emerson. "Nothing can bring you happiness but yourself." I went inside and bought a huge Walnut Springs country ham, had it sliced and headed for Skeeter's Restaurant. I suddenly remembered that I had eaten five helpings of Velma Jane's banana pudding at the family reunion.

Moonshine and Ginseng

Another family storyteller, my Great-Uncle Luke, said that his daddy, my Great-Great-Uncle Abner Mason, made the best moonshine in the Appalachian Mountains. Truth be told, he was the Popcorn Sutton of Macon County; however, Uncle Abner was producing his product fifty years before Popcorn was born. Being a good Baptist, he never drank the stuff himself, except to sample each run as it came out of the pipe. As I've said before, one can argue about what amount constitutes a sample.

Back in those days, the ATF concentrated its efforts mostly on major producers of illicit alcohol. They rarely bothered the small producer, especially if said producer lived back in the wilderness coves of Appalachia. Still, any man-Jack who made his living from liquid corn was aware of the ATF and took precautions accordingly.

Uncle Abner was no exception.

He never kept a gun at his still because he understood that a shootout with the ATF, if that happened, would probably be a losing proposition. But there was another reason. Being part Cherokee, he could shoot the eye out of a flying duck with an arrow.

Uncle Luke said that Abner could sit on the hill next to his still, and with his bow, drive a shaft into a half-dozen men before they knew what was happening. Fortunately, he never had to do so. He used his considerable skills to take down an occasional deer or wild hog that happened to wander by.

Uncle Luke said that Abner's still was so well hidden that a bear would have trouble finding it even if the mash barrel was filled with honey. If Luke knew the location of his daddy's still, he died with the secret.

In those days, the Nantahala Community was wild country and only the hardiest of pioneers could negotiate their way around the hundreds of creeks and coves. As it were, most moonshiners liked to grow their corn near their still, but apparently Abner didn't. Back then it was hard to find someone not in bed by 9:00 p.m. That is, except Abner. He had a team of mules and the occasional Nantahala citizen would awaken to hear the clop-clop of hooves after midnight. No one knew where he was going and no one was dumb enough to follow him because he could hear a pin drop at a hundred yards. This was probably not true, but that's what people believed and sometimes perception is everything.

There were a lot of stories about Uncle Abner that floated around, but usually they were told in quiet company. For the most part, people in Nantahala believed in minding their own business. Any outsider who tried to pry into the business of one of the local folk was met with total silence and often, disdain. It was believed, but not proven, that Abner's mother was the sister of Cherokee Chief Yonaguska. Too, it was well known that Abner had more in common with the Cherokee than his blood line. He sold firewater to the Indians for some time until Chief Standing Deer called him in to his lodge and explained that he wasn't doing his brethren any favors. From that point on, Abner found other customers. He just sold more to the Charleston (now Bryson City) folk which was easier anyway since that community was closer.

Abner made his way into Charleston by taking his mules across Happy Top, on through Grassy Branch and down through "Larky," now called the Alarka Community. Early one March, he set out with twelve gallons on each mule. The trail was so narrow that he had to lead his mules single file. Just as he started down the mountain, he got caught in a blizzard. He couldn't find a cave but he did find an overhanging rock that jutted out far enough from the cliff face to afford some protection. He was stuck there for six days. By the third day, he and the mules were eating leaves and bark to survive. He melted water and mixed moonshine with it to keep himself and the mules from freezing. It worked and when he reached Charleston, he still had sixteen gallons.

He was also one of the pioneers who blazed a trail across the Tusquitee Mountains into Quanassae (later Hayesville) and points south. One story went that as he made his way down the mountain toward

Hayesville, something began spooking his mules. At first he saw nothing and heard nothing, but he was quite sure he was being followed by a panther. He feared that if the panther got close enough, the mules would panic and run, and in the process, destroy his week's work.

Just as he rounded a turn in the trail, the panther attacked. Uncle Abner shot at it and missed. He turned the rifle around, grabbed it by the barrel and hit the panther across the side of its head with the stock. That stunned it and caused it to stop momentarily. His lead mule kicked the critter and damaged it severely. While it lay there panting, Abner whipped out his hunting knife and slit its throat. When the ruckus was over, he skinned the panther, hung the hide on a high limb to dry and collected it on the way back. He was one of the few men in Nantahala who had a panther hide nailed to his barn wall.

One time, a fellow by the name of Lewis Redmond, who lived in the Maple Springs section of Macon County (later to become Swain County) just off what is now known as Needmore Road, started telling people that Abner's moonshine would make the drinker go blind. Abner couldn't figure out why the fellow would tell people that. Everybody had told him that he made the best shine east of the Mississippi. When his business began to suffer, he decided to track the fellow down and find out why he was telling lies about his product. As it turned out, Lewis was an outlaw and a moonshiner, and he felt threatened by Abner's intrusion into his territory.

When Uncle Abner arrived at Redmond's shack,

the man ordered him off his property with a gun. Not wishing to start a fuss, he turned around and rode his mule back down the road.

A few days later, Redmond went up the branch to work his still and found several arrows in his boiler and mash barrels. He went around threatening to kill Abner. Early one morning, he walked down the trail to the outhouse for his morning constitution. When he came out, he found himself surrounded by Indians. He was told in no uncertain terms to leave Abner alone or they would tie him up and put him in a cage with a hungry panther. Nothing much scared Redmond but that did. A couple years later, he went to prison for several infractions of the law in addition to moonshining, but that's another story.

On his 50th birthday, Uncle Abner retired from his moonshining business. He said thirty years of avoiding the law was enough. The ginseng market was starting to take hold and he turned his efforts to combing the mountains for that elusive herb. As it turned out, he made a better living doing that than he had at making shine, and it wasn't illegal, at least it wasn't back then. About ten years later, on a foggy morning, he fell to his death on the Winding Stairs when he inadvertently wandered off the trail. Some of the folks at his funeral wondered why so many people from Swain and Clay Counties attended. They had forgotten his past but his customers hadn't.

Three Rednecks and a Dozer

On the way back from the beach, I decided to stop off and visit my cousin, Mayberle, in Arapahoe, North Carolina. I probably should mention that Arapahoe was founded by two settlers who got ticked off at the people who founded New Bern. They applied to the Postal Service to name their new community Bethany Crossroads. When they learned that their chosen name was already taken, they decided to name the place after the founder's favorite horse, Arapahoe. After 125 years of growth, the community now has about 400 people. As far as I know, the only other town named after a horse is Horse Prairie, Montana. I spent a week there one night, but that's another story.

Mayberle had married a Pamlico River rat by the name of Jimmy Don Pervis. In that neck of the woods, a river rat is a redneck who spends his days fishing for carp and catfish and his nights frog gigging in a float boat. Somewhere along the way, Mayberle had nicknamed him Froggy. He had lost two of his upper front teeth in a fight with another swamp rat; consequently, he whistled when he talked. On the other hand, Mayberle had been named Miss Pamlico River three years in a row. I later learned that it wasn't a complimentary title but nobody had told her. She had been awarded a tee shirt with Pamlico across the front. Whoever had screen printed it couldn't spell and it read "Pamico Rivor." I never did find out if no one had mentioned it because they were being kind or because none of them could spell either. For example, Froggy had dropped out of school in the fifth grade and Mayberle, who had been good in math, couldn't spell her way out of a paper bag.

When I arrived, I found them removing the underpinning from their single wide. I asked if they were getting ready to move and Froggy said, "Ther-r-re's your sign."

Mayberle told me that I had arrived just in time to help. A few minutes later, Froggy's brother, Amster, started backing his old Dodge dually up to the trailer. He jumped out of the truck and they began the task of hooking up. It was like watching Shemp, Larry and Moe move a chicken house with the chickens in it. Froggy dropped a cinder block on his foot and Amster mashed his hand trying to hook up the tow bar. Mayberle was inside the trailer trying to get lunch started. I saw smoke coming out the window so I ran inside to see if I could help. Since the electricity was disconnected, she had almost set the kitchen on fire trying to light the gas stove with a match and a rolled up newspaper. I asked her why she didn't just light the gas with the match and she said that she didn't want to get her hand that close to the stove. I got the burner started and then suggested that next time she should use just one page of the paper, not the entire Sunday edition.

After about an hour of mechanical mishaps and severe abuse of the English language, Froggy and Amster got the trailer rolling. I left Mayberle to her cooking and followed along in my truck. The trip took about fifteen minutes to the new location. Much to my surprise, it was a beautiful lot with a lot of yaupon and live oak trees. After walking around and surveying the site, Amster started backing the trailer into their chosen space. When he backed into a tree for the third time, Mayberle came out and taught her brother-in-law some new words. Just when I thought he was going to get the trailer in the right spot, she decided that she wanted it parked about fifty feet farther back and to the right.

If looks could kill, she would have been dead on the spot. The two men spent about thirty minutes getting a balky chain saw started so they could cut off several limbs that were in the way. Amster started backing up again but lost his nerve when he tried to make the turn between two trees.

Mayberle decided to come out and supervise which just made the situation worse. Not being a shrinking violet, Amster just said straight out that he wasn't taking orders from a woman. Telling him that it was her trailer didn't help any. After about five minutes of yelling at each other, they decided to try another approach. Froggy wanted to cut one of the trees down, but Mayberle said, "Over my dead body;" to which Froggy replied, "Don't tempt me."

Deciding to take the risk, I stuck my nose in and suggested that they needed a third party, preferably one who owned a bulldozer. Fortunately, a friend of Froggy's was clearing some land about a mile down the road so he headed out to find him. Mayberle went back to her cooking. In about an hour I saw a semi coming up the road with a bulldozer loaded on the back. The friend's name was Ervin who started out by cutting off a chunk of Brown's Mule chewing tobacco and stuffing his jaw. I immediately dubbed him "Gomer," but not to his face. He drove the dozer off the truck and the three men gathered around to assess the situation. They came to a decision and Gomer hooked up to the towbar. He climbed back on the dozer, and then leaned over and spat a stream of tobacco juice at a unicorn beetle. The big bug scurried for cover.

Gomer may have been a high school dropout but he sure knew how to operate heavy equipment. He pulled the trailer back out in the direction it had been brought in. He straightened up and then started backing as fast as the dozer would go. I just knew there was going to be a horrible accident, so I held my breath. The trailer zipped through between the two trees with about two inches on each side. With a lurch, he brought the trailer to a halt exactly where it was supposed to go.

The sudden stop caused Mayberle's seafood chowder to slosh over on the stove. She rushed out

waving a big butcher knife and threatening to eliminate Gomer's chances of having children. When she
saw that he had placed the trailer exactly where she
wanted it, she smiled from ear-to-ear.

She and Froggy put a folding table out under a
tree and I helped bring out the late lunch. The food
was delicious and her cornbread was even better. Obviously, Aunt Bessie had taught her well. We all over-
ate and then sat around and talked for a while.

Gomer loaded up his dozer and headed down the
road to scare someone else.

Mayberle and Froggy invited me to spend the
night but I declined. I was afraid Mayberle might decide to move the trailer again while I was asleep.

CHAPTER THREE
Mountain Medicine

Life Without a Doctor

I have used the term "mountain medicine" rather than "folk medicine" because the latter term covers a much broader range of time and geography. I am referring to the Great Smoky Mountains in particular and the Southern Appalachians in general. In view of this, I will try to relate how mountain folk tried, sometimes successfully and sometimes not, to heal their sick. I make no claim that any of my information is the gospel truth, but it is as accurate as I could make it.

In addition to my own knowledge and memories, I have gleaned as much as possible from various sources. Written and published information is often sketchy, and one source frequently conflicts with another. Knowledge of mountain medicine was passed down from one generation to the next by word of mouth. Recipes for herbal remedies were rarely written down, and because of this, huge amounts of information have been lost forever. To say the least, I was surprised to find that there is not much useful published literature. Anthony Cavender, Professor of Anthropology at East Tennessee State University, published a book entitled Folk Medicine in Southern Appalachia. The book is well-organized, highly researched and contains a lot of information. Unfortunately, it was written for academic consumption and is so riddled with scholarly terms and phrases as to make it frustrating and confusing to the average reader. Despite the difficulty, I was able to glean some useful material from his book which I used to corroborate other sources.

In the absence of doctors, Nantahala and Burningtown people, like most of Appalachia and other remote regions of the country, gathered medicinal plants and processed them in a variety of ways to use in the treatment of disease, both minor and major. Although doctors were available in urbanized areas, mountain people did not use them for a number of reasons. The two major reasons were lack of access and cost. Specifically, rural people had no viable transportation and no money.

When my grandmother was a child, the nearest doctor might as well have been a million miles away. Interestingly, Nantahala did not have a doctor then and does not have one now. Of course, there is a major difference. If my great-grandfather had taken a sick child to a doctor in Franklin, it would have taken two days by horse and wagon. Today, my cousins can drive my Aunt Frances from Camp Branch to a doctor in Andrews in forty-five minutes or less.

For the purpose of this essay, a mountain doctor

was anyone schooled in the use of herbal medicines. The doctor may have been a medical professional, but was more likely a grandmother who took time to learn the fine art of gathering, preparing and storing medicinal plants. Some of our mountain medicines came over from Europe, some were borrowed from the Cherokee or other Native-Americans and some were learned through trial and error.

The Appalachian Mountains is one of the best locations in the world for the natural growth of medicinal herbs. It is now known that there are over a thousand plant species that can be used for healing powers in some form or another. It's no wonder then, that both Cherokee and European-descent grandmothers became herbal specialists.

Until the early 1900's, doctors used medicines that were very similar to those used by people at home or by the community herbalists. Of the many medicinal plants available, only about one hundred or so were actually used in practice, and the major list was probably thirty or less. Treatments for diseases varied somewhat from region to region, but in the main, mountain medicine was similar throughout Appalachia.

Doctors and grandmothers prepared medicines in much the same way. They mashed the herbs into a paste, squeezed them to extract their juices, steeped them in either hot or cold water or ground them into a powder. When they used the powder, they would mix it with a liquid, roll it into a pill or blow it into the sick person's throat with a quill or rolled-up paper.

Often they made syrup by mixing the herb with

honey, molasses or sugar. They also packed them into a poultice or made a salve or ointment by mixing with petroleum jelly, butter, lard or another medium.

Patent medicines thrived in those days and were sold throughout the country. Although there were hundreds on the market, mostly in northern cities, only a handful made their way into the Appalachian Mountains. Some of them were directed to specific ailments. Others were billed as a cure all for every disease known to man. A few of them performed as advertised but most were a total waste of money and sometimes did more harm than good.

Men were seldom the expert in the family when it came to medical treatment although there were a few male herbalists scattered about in the Appalachian Mountains. In the seventeenth through the nineteenth century, the majority of medical practitioners were older women who had spent their lives trying to cure their families and neighbors. As modern medicine became more advanced, people began to rely more on doctors and less on the old herbalists. In today's world, those old medical practitioners are almost extinct. They have been replaced by an industry called homeopathy which sells everything from acupuncture to massage.

The remainder of this section will focus on herbal teas. In general, they were prepared by boiling the roots, stems or leaves of medicinal plants such as catnip, yellow root or boneset. Often they were administered as soon as they were cool enough to drink. These were called "teas" regardless of the plant used.

Some of the most common teas were catnip, yellow root, boneset and sassafras. Mom and my aunts were strong believers in catnip tea. It was used to treat colic in babies and stomach ache in adults. Sometimes, it was used to reduce fever. Mom also took it for nerves, and she used it in a poultice for sprains, cuts and bruises. Often, she would drink it before bedtime to help her drop off to sleep. Another advantage of catnip tea is that is doesn't taste bitter like some of the other teas. Because of this, it was easier to administer to children.

Yellow root is another of the herbs that can be made into a tea. One has to be careful because it is toxic in large doses. Wild animals know this and won't eat it. Probably, its most common use was for stomach and mouth ulcers. Certainly, it was a proven stomach medicine. My grandmother Rosa used it, and so did her daughters. It was a favorite of the Cherokee for skin ailments and as an antiseptic for cuts and bruises.

I know my mother used sassafras tea for colds. When steeped properly, it actually tastes good. Only the young roots should be used to make the tea. As a mountain medicine, it was also used to treat rheumatism, a variety of skin diseases, low blood and dropsy. In recent years, it has been determined that sassafras oil, the part that activates the tea, is carcinogenic. It's possible that this medicine did more harm than good, but mountain healers had the ability to use the proper amount to match the malady. Like many other herbs, its successful use was a result of centuries of trial and error.

In earlier years, boneset had many uses. In the

absence of aspirin, it was used to reduce fever. It was used as an all-around tonic because it was believed, and to some extent rightly so, that it acted on the liver, bowels and stomach. It was especially useful for stomach problems of all kinds. Folk doctors learned to vary the strength which made it useful for several maladies. It was one of the most common herbs used by Native Americans for many infectious diseases and fever-related problems.

The actual list of herbal teas used by mountain folk is quite lengthy. Dandelion was used to stimulate and cleanse the liver. It was also believed to reduce or eliminate gallstones. Burdock root tea was used to cleanse the blood and to stimulate the liver. Yarrow, which grew everywhere, was used to combat chest congestion and colds. For someone who wasn't eating well, it was used to stimulate the appetite. Fennel was used for the same reasons as yarrow with the added ability to soothe sore throats and coughs. Raspberry leaf was used to reduce diarrhea and ease menstrual cramps. Strawberry was used for the same reason as raspberry, and was also believed to relieve arthritis and rheumatism. The small ends of blackberry roots were used to curb diarrhea. Mint teas were used for stomach disorders and headaches. Too, they were the "pleasure herb" of the mountain folk because they were often consumed just for the pleasant smell and taste. They were especially enjoyable on cold winter days when families were confined to the house. It was considered pure pleasure to sit in a rocker in front of a blazing fire and sip peppermint or spearmint tea.

Over time, herbal doctors learned that teas were

the best delivery system for the body's efficient use. The human system would absorb them better than if they were ingested as a powder or a solid. Boiling and then steeping created a natural interaction between the components of the herb. This brought out both the flavor and the medicinal qualities. When used properly, the sick got well faster. Unfortunately some teas had a bitter taste and were often improved by adding sugar or molasses. In any event, there was once a wide belief among mountain people that "bitter" tasting teas were better for a sick person. Also, they believed that the bitter taste stimulated the taste buds which in turn stimulated digestion.

Both my grandmothers doctored their children with "teas" steeped from plants they either grew or found on their own property. Between them, they raised sixteen children who lived to a ripe old age. My four great-grandmothers raised almost forty children between them, and I doubt any one of them every saw a doctor. I find this simply amazing.

A Gift From God

Genesis 1:29 reads, *"And God said, behold, I have given you every herb bearing seed, which is upon the face of all the earth, and every tree, in which is the fruit of a tree yielding seed; to you it shall be for meat."* Clearly, herbs were set apart from the beginning as a benefit to mankind. A number of herbs and plants are mentioned by name in the Bible. We are familiar with a few, but most we are not. Some of them may be the same as those used by our grandmothers, but it is difficult to tell because the names are different, and the Bible doesn't go into enough detail to get a good match.

In our grandmother's time, mountain medicines were considered a gift from God for two reasons. The first is that it's true, and the second is because that's all they had. Many of the teas and powders had already been used by Cherokee women for hundreds of years. By and large, mountain folk got along well with the Cherokee, especially the women who were quick to adopt many of their time-proven remedies.

This second section will focus primarily on the powders. If stored properly, they could be kept for months or in some cases, years. The diseases and discomforts accompanying each herb listed below are by no means inclusive, and as such, are intended to give the reader a general idea about how mountain people used powdered roots, leaves and berries to heal their sick before the advent of modern medicine. Many of them were used for the same malady. Their use was, in part, determined by their availability. For example, a particular plant might be plentiful in one area of The Smoky Mountains but not in another and vice-versa. Also, one might be available in the spring and another in the fall.

Many of these remedies were successful or thought to be so, while others were sometimes ineffective. Because the same disease and the curative powers of a particular herb varied from person to person, people usually didn't know for sure if the remedy helped or if they would have gotten well anyway as a result of the body's natural defenses. Too, they were not skilled in data gathering which is essential in the determination of any drug's curative powers.

If used improperly, they were harmful in the same way that today's prescription medicines are dangerous if not used as directed. A few of these remedies were used by my parents when I had some type of illness. A longer list was used by my grandparents to treat my parents. Others not used by my family were used in the general Appalachian community. This list is those herbs used most often. There were many others, of course, but a complete accounting would take several pages and is not in the best interest of this essay. By the way, don't use any of these without consulting your grandmother.

Arrowroot – *stomach disorders.*
Barberry – *stomach tonic, regulates digestion, eases inflammation and infection of the urinary tract, sore throat, nasal congestion and yeast infection.*
Bilberry – *lowering blood sugar and treating diabetes, diarrhea, and eye disorders.*
Black cohosh – *malaria, rheumatism, sore throat, constipation, hives and backache.*
Black walnut hulls (green) – *help control and eliminate parasites from the body.*
Bloodroot – *treating skin aliments such as ringworm, warts and fungal infections. Also as a cure for rash caused by poison ivy, poison oak and sumac.*
Chickweed – *colds, coughs and healing ointments. This yard pest contains more vitamins and minerals than most greens, and makes a healthy salad.*
Corn silk tea – *bedwetting.*
Dogwood bark – *loss of appetite.*
Feverfew – *fever, headaches and arthritis.*
Ginseng – *physical and mental endurance and increased energy. Because of its value in other cultures, it was and still is one of the most sought after plants for its commercial value.*
Golden seal (yellow root) – *Bronchitis, eye infections, improve digestion, and female problems.*
Mayapple root – *laxative, kill parasites. May be in the same family of plants as the mandrakes mentioned in*

Genesis 30:14-16.
Nettle leaves – *rheumatism, arthritis and gout.*
Plantain leaves – *diaper rash, bug bites and skin irritation, good in salads.*
Slippery elm – *wounds, ulcers, burns, cough, sore throat, and upset stomach.*
Solomon's seal root – *indigestion and lung ailments.*
White oak bark – *menstrual problems and varicose veins.*
Wild yam root – *menstrual cramps, nausea and morning sickness.*
Willow bark – *arthritis.*

I know from experience that arrowroot will settle an upset stomach. I used to buy barberry lozenges in a health food store in Hickory. They were very good for sore throat. I have rubbed bloodroot on poison ivy inflammation with considerable success. I have used ginseng for extra energy when I started slowing down on the job. It works for that, but I doubt that it is useful for much else. I know for a fact that eating too many mayapples will send one to the woods so I'm sure it's effective for constipation.

I had ringworm once, and I think Dad rubbed mayapple root on it to make it go away. I knew a lady in the Boone area that used powdered nettle leaves for gout, and she claimed that it helped a great deal. I have rubbed plantain leaves on bug bites and bee stings. I know Mom drank dandelion tea, but I don't know why for sure. Female matters were not discussed in family circles when I was a kid.

Unfortunately, there isn't space to go into detail

about a particular medicinal plant. Encyclopedias, dictionaries and herbal books are good sources. One can go on the internet, inquire on mountain medicine or folk medicine and end up with a long list of people selling something. Their sales pitches are carefully worded to sound good but their usefulness is questionable at best.

All of the herbs listed above and many more are sold in health food stores today. In the old days, they were processed by people who cared about sickness, and because of this, they took great pains to make the purest medicine possible. By and large, producers today care about money, and one may or may not get the strength advertised. I think, in many cases, if properly used in a known strength, a lot of herbal remedies are as good, and in some cases better, than their pharmaceutical counterparts. Unfortunately, doctors do not take them seriously because today's medical remedies are controlled by corporate giants.

Just recently, I visited a doctor, and there were more pharmaceutical salesmen in the lobby than there were patients. To give credit where credit is due, there are some excellent drugs in today's market that have saved the lives of many patients and alleviated pain and sickness in many more.

In any event, the purpose of this essay is to inform the reader about medicines used by those who came before us. They knew a great deal about what medicinal actions these herbs would produce. They probably never heard the word "astringent" in their lives, but they knew blackberry root or slippery elm would cause tissue to contract.

They didn't know "carminative" from a door knob, but they knew that arrowroot, catnip and peppermint would support and soothe the digestive system.

They knew nothing about diuretics, but they knew that burdock, butcher's broom and dandelion would relieve water retention. They knew that cohosh and ginger would promote menstrual flow. They knew that boneset, willow bark and garlic would reduce fever. They knew a lot of things that today's medical profession has forgotten or ignored, but most importantly, they loved the people they treated, and they helped friends and family survive at a time when nothing else was available.

Detailed below is a list passed on to my wife, Nita Welch Owenby, from her Grandparents, Deck and Cordie Welch, and is believed to have been written by her Great-Grandpa Lafayette (Fate) Welch. He was a horseback doctor who treated people in and around Rose Creek, Burningtown, Cowee and Oak Grove.

Sweetened raw onion juice *is good for croup.*
Crushed onion *applied to a burn or scald will draw out the fire.*
Garlic eaten raw *is good for high blood pressure.*
Okra boiled *is good for pain due to stomach ulcers.*
Irish potatoes *boiled with the skins on and put on hot is good for inflammatory rheumatism.*
Horse radish roots *made into a tea is also good for rheumatism.*
Sage tea *is good for sore throat, and if take frequently, it is good for night sweats.*

Sauerkraut *is a good liver medicine and also relieves constipation.*
Peach tree leaf tea *will stop vomiting.*
Ragweed tea *will stop diarrhea.*
Huckleberry leaves *is considered good for diabetes.*
Plantain and coltsfoot *relieves the symptoms of consumption.*
Dried elder flowers *will break out the measles.*

My Great-Uncle John Owenby was an herbalist by choice and interest, but not as a profession. He knew a great deal about herbs, where to find them, how to preserve them and how to use them. I believe his mother, Adeline Ervin Owenby, got him started, and he just continued to learn.

His medical abilities went beyond the practice of using herbal remedies. He could look in a person's eyes and tell if he or she had measles before breaking out. He could take a crick out of someone's neck, a procedure that is normally done by a chiropractor or a physical therapist today. He did not doctor the Nantahala community at large but only his family and friends.

As I said in Part I, women were by far, the majority of healers in the 1800's and early 1900's, but Uncle John was one of the exceptions. He was another one of those who didn't write anything down, and that's a shame, because he could have contributed much to the practice of mountain medicine.

Patent Medicines

Colds were one of the most common treated maladies when my grandmothers were children. This is one human disease that modern medicine has done nothing to improve on, and no cure is in sight. When I was a kid, a common treatment for colds was to put a drop or two of Camphor on a lump of sugar. Camphor is like aspirin; a little is useful but too much can cause severe damage or kill. It has a pain relieving effect for external use and was often used in liniments.

Mom's medicine of choice was to get out the Vicks Salve and rub it on my chest or put it in a pot of boiling water and have me inhale the vapors with a towel over my head. I still use this remedy when high-priced prescription medicine doesn't work. I can remember watching my Grandma Rosa rub the salve in her nose before bedtime.

And of course, the ladies in my family cooked up homemade chicken soup for colds, flu and croup.

Often, the soup was so good that the rest of the family had to be stopped from eating it up. Even today, doctors sometimes recommend chicken soup. The steam from the soup helps unstop swollen nasal passages, reduces sinus drainage and soothes a sore throat. There are hundreds of cold remedies on the market and most of them are not any better than chicken soup. In fact, many of them do nothing at all except lighten the weight of one's wallet or purse.

Flu was, for all intents and purposes, treated the same way as colds and pneumonia. In the 1800s, people were often wrapped up in blankets to make them sweat it out. Unfortunately, this often drove the fever higher, and the person died. In the 1900's, people learned that cold would help reduce fever. Cold rocks from a creek or even snow was used.

The great flu epidemic of 1918 killed millions of people throughout the United States and the world. Certainly, people of Appalachia died from it. Ethel Welch said that her mom and dad, Sally and Cling Roper, got the flu, along with her brother and sister, Bronce and Maud. Ethel was only seven in 1918. Sally told her how to make teas from the herbs she had collected and dried. There was a big snow on the ground, and they ran out of wood for the fireplace. Ethel and her younger brother, T.C. climbed up in the loft where old shoes were kept and threw them down to keep the fire going. She said it was days before anyone got to their house, and several men in the Burningtown Community brought them wood. Fortunately, all the sick recovered.

When I was eight years old, I contacted the itch

(scabies) at school. Scabies is caused by a mite that burrows into the skin. It is not life threatening, but it can make one very uncomfortable. It is also highly contagious. My Dad rubbed a mixture of butter and sulfur on me. The butter was a binder to keep the sulfur in a uniform mixture. Lard worked just as well as butter. It all depended on what was available at the time. The sulfur is what killed the mite. My parents kept me home from school for about a week. Scabies is sometimes caused by unsanitary conditions, but this was not the case with my infestation. My grandmother, my mother and my aunts were fanatics about cleanliness. We didn't have much in creature comforts, but we had soap and bleach. While commercial bleach became available in 1816, lye soap covered the germ killing properties of both.

The one time I had head lice, it seems that Dad put a mixture of lard and kerosene on my head. He believed in the healing power of kerosene. It is carcinogenic in long term use, but he didn't know that. The most common method of removing lice was multiple combings with a very fine tooth comb. Another method was to coat the head with Vaseline or apply a solution of mineral oil, baby oil and vinegar.

Curing hiccups had about the same cures that people try today. One cure that actually worked and still does is to swallow a teaspoonful of sugar. Often we kids would pretend to have hiccups so we could get a spoonful. Another method was to scare or startle someone. Sometimes the cure was worse than the disease because if the scare was successful, it had other side effects such as a temporary bad case of nerves. Other methods were to breathe into a paper bag, drink ten sips of water without breathing or slowly counting to ten without breathing. Babies would often get hiccups, and the cure was to carry them upside down. I never heard of a baby being hurt by this method, but it certainly had the potential to do so. Most of the time, hiccups will go away in a short time if they are just ignored.

Menstrual problems were a subject not discussed in mixed company or around children. I learned about it by eavesdropping on the women when they thought I wasn't listening. If a woman's menstrual flow was stopped for some reason, it was considered dangerous. Red pepper tea was used to restart and was reputed to be successful. If a woman had a heavy flow, cherry bark tea was used to reduce it. A whole host of other teas were used to start, stop or reduce the flow, but because of the hush-hush nature of this natural occurrence in all women, information was scanty at best.

An article about mountain medicine would not be complete without some information about "patent medicines." This was a misnomer because they were not actually patented. Most of them claimed secret formulas, and in fact, many of their ingredients were never known. They often contained dangerous levels of opium, alcohol and other narcotic ingredients. In the 1800's, people did not trust doctors, and often with good reason. The patent medicine industry took advantage of this and advertised their products heavily. In addition to their cure alls, they often printed flyers and monthly almanacs that provided information to rural people. Of course, their purpose was to support and increase the sale of their products.

One of the magazines that reached Nantahala was the Grit. It was published independently of the patent industry but relied heavily on their advertisements for financial support. When I was a boy, it was delivered to Flossie Grant and shared with my mom and grandmother. They in turn shared it with others. The majority of patent medicine's claims was blatant lies and was eventually taken to task by the Federal Trade Commission.There were hundreds sold through out the United States. Listed below are a few that were popular in the Appalachians.

Black Draught – *A purified mixture of the natural glycosides derived from a plant of the bearberry family and used as a laxative. This mixture is also an ingredient in commercial Castor Oil.*

Carter's Little Liver Pills – *The main ingredient was dried mayapple root and dried aloe juice. The pills had nothing to do with the liver, but it was a mild laxative. It was first produced by Dr. Samuel Carter of Erie, Pa. in 1868. They supposedly cured sick head-ache, biliousness, constipation and bad complexion. There was a ten year battle between the FTC and Carter to remove the word liver and stop claiming the pills were a cure for anything except sluggish bowels. It is still sold as Carter's Pills and now contains bisacodyl, the same ingredient used in Dulcolax.*

Cardui – *Contained 19% percent alcohol. It was sold primarily as a home treatment for women's diseases and painful menstruation. Given the alcohol content, it* *certainly did reduce pain if consumed in quantity. It also contained distilled milk thistle which also reduces pain so their claims weren't totally false. It was produced by the Chattanooga Medicine Company, and a large part of their advertising success was due to testimonials by women who had used the product.*

Dr. Thatcher's Liver and Blood Syrup – *Produced by the Thatcher Medicine Company of Chattanooga, Tennessee. It was billed as a laxative or cathartic, according to the dose. A cathartic is a product that energizes or makes one feel good. To this extent, the syrup was successful because it contained nine percent alcohol.*

Dr. Miles Nervine – *A product of Dr. Miles Medical Company founded in 1884 by Franklin Miles. It was billed as treating all nervous ailments including nervousness or nervous exhaustion, sleeplessness, hysteria, headache, neuralgia, backache, pain, epilepsy, spasms, fits and St. Vitus' dance. He also published Medical News which was another of the flyers that primarily promoted his product. He also published Dr. Miles New Weather Almanac and Handbook of Valuable Information. Of course, this too, was a front for selling his Nervine tonic. It too, contained alcohol.*

Blair's Liniment or Dr. Blair's High Power Liniment – *It was produced by Blair Laboratories of Lynchburg, Virginia. The two primary ingredients were menthol and menthol salicylate. It was sold for all external ailments such as cuts, bruises and abrasions, muscle aches and pain of arthritis. Blair also sold a gout and rheumatism pill.*

Rosebud Salve – *First sold by the Rosebud Perfume Company in 1892. It was advertised as a cure-all for* *all skin blemishes, chapped lips and dry elbows. It is a petrolatum based balm with cottonseed oil, borax and seven different rose oils. Its pink color and pleasant smell made it popular among women. The salve is still sold today primarily as a lip balm. It has had a large following every since it was put on the market even though it has been one of the least advertised products among the patent medicines. Rosebud claims that they have never changed it since the day it was first sold. The Rosebud Company is still family owned.*

Cloverine Salve – *Developed by Dr. James Wilson in 1860. He originally created it for his patients. It was and still is sold for chapped hands, dry and rough skin, and minor burns. It was advertised as "Refreshing like a cool, clover-scented meadow." It is neutral to whitish in color and doesn't smell as good as Rosebud, but it doesn't smell bad, either.*

A lot of the patent medicines became a morally acceptable way to use alcohol for a variety of ailments. Alcohol, when used properly, was a good sedative and pain reliever. It was as true then as it is today that people will try almost anything when they are desperate for pain relief. Probably, the best patent medicines were those that still survive. Whether they were actually helpful or not, they were an important part of mountain medicine.

Communicable Diseases

When I visit the cemeteries in Nantahala, I am reminded that the good old days weren't always good. I am always saddened by the number of children's graves, and most of them are unmarked. The cause of those graves and my mother's paranoia about cleanliness had their roots in the same problem; disease. In the 1800's, childbirth and childhood diseases were often caused by unsanitary conditions. People did not dispose of waste properly; they did not clean childbirth rooms, bedclothes, dishes and other utensils very well. They had no idea that disease was caused by germs and therefore, saw no reason for cleanliness. Even doctors did not believe that cleanliness was associated with sickness and death. Once the connection was made, deaths went down tenfold.

By the time my grandparents began having children, the word had been passed, and they became true believers. This did not stop all disease, of course. A meticulously clean person could contact typhoid fever or smallpox from someone who carried it if they came in contact with the infected person. Once infected, all the cleanliness in the world would not stop it. Herbal treatments that worked well for many other ailments did little to stop those diseases. Often, the best that people could do was to make the sick as comfortable as possible and hope for the best. In areas where serum became available, these diseases were stopped in their tracks.

In the Appalachian Mountains, the delivery of babies was still handled by old grannies and mid-wives. Some of them had not been convinced of the necessity for extreme cleanliness. It is my under-standing, that Elender Passmore, who delivered most of the Nantahala babies, including me, for over forty years, used lots of boiling water to sterilize everything that touched the mothers or babies. My dad told me that the first thing Elender did when she walked into a birth room was to make sure that plenty of boiling water was available. I don't know if she did this in her earlier years, but somewhere along the way, she came to understand the dangers of bacteria. I'm convinced that the hot water she used saved the lives of many mothers and their newborn children.

Too often, people believed that diseases were sent on them because of some infraction of morals or even a family curse. Unfortunately, there was and still are family curses due to some imperfection in family gene makeup, but at least now, we understand where the problems are coming from. Both of my grand-mothers lost children to childhood diseases. In gen-eral, people had no idea where germs and viruses originated and even less knowledge of how to deal with them.

Crib deaths, which people knew nothing about at the time, were often blamed on the mothers. Newborn babies usually slept with the mothers for ease of nursing. Bottle feeding was rarely used. Other people and the mothers themselves often thought that they had rolled over on the babies and smothered them.

Back before some of our modern drugs were invented, typhoid, influenza, scarlet fever, diphtheria, small pox and pneumonia struck without warning. The communicable diseases spread faster in urban areas such as Knoxville, Asheville, and Charlotte. Even so, the mountainous regions had their share of these diseases. Usually, they struck an area such as Spruce Pine, Burningtown or Nantahala when they were carried in by an outsider. In a small community, most residents attended one or two churches. People touched and hugged, used the same privy and drank from the same dipper at the spring behind the church. Too often, those diseases were spread by people trying to help the infected, not knowing that they were carrying the diseases to other people.

Typhoid fever is a bacterial infection of the intestinal tract or the blood stream. It is a strain of Salmonella. The germs are spread by drinking water or eating foods contaminated by people who have the disease. Almost all households in Appalachia had a common dipper used to drink water from a bucket or a spring. Also, every home had an outside toilet. While people usually washed their hands after a visit to the outhouse, common materials were handled while they were in the privy. Because of this, it was often too late to wash their hands upon returning to the house; the germs had already been passed.

Children had a higher risk of dying from this disease than adults did. A common treatment was sweating. This was accomplished in two ways. One was to bundle the sick person in several blankets or quilts and put them in a room with a fireplace. The other was with herbs such as mustard seeds and lobelia. Too, people believed that they could purge the body of disease by giving them castor oil with a couple drops of turpentine. Onions were hung on the walls in hopes of preventing the disease.

Diphtheria is a disease of the upper respiratory tract. It is highly contagious. Its initial symptoms are similar to the flu. Untreated, as it generally was in those days, the infected individual's blood pressure dropped, their pulse rate increased and they reached a point when they couldn't swallow.

Some of the remedies in the 1800s ranged from useless to deadly. For example, a poultice of salt pork and sliced onions on the neck, burn a mixture of turpentine and tar by the sick person's bed or sucking on a mixture of sulfur and mercury. Children rarely recovered, and although adults had a better chance, many of them didn't recover either. In the 1920s, deaths from this terrible disease averaged 150,000 people per year in the U.S. Macon County certainly had its share of death from this disease as did the rest of the surrounding counties.

The annual Iditarod dog race in Alaska is a result of a desperate race to get the antitoxin to Nome,

Alaska. The now famous, "mushers," raced their dogs around the clock, risking their lives and the lives of their dogs to get to Nome in time to save the remaining citizens from dying of this horrible disease. Their unbelievable heroism saved the lives of those who had not already contracted diphtheria.

Another of the killer diseases was smallpox. It was introduced into the America's by the Spanish. It is believed this disease killed over a million Aztecs. The British gave it to the Cherokee in the mid 1700's and wiped out a large segment of their population. Smallpox broke out in various places in Appalachia until the early 1900s. It usually occurred where there were a large group of people together such as wood camps or mining operations. Knoxville was hit hard. When the vaccine found its way into the mountains; the epidemics were stopped. Unfortunately, it was often too late. Sometimes, people made their children wear a red flannel bag of asafetida around their necks to ward off smallpox. It only helped to prevent the disease in that it smelled so bad that people wouldn't come close to the person wearing the bag.

Smallpox was most often spread by direct contact with body fluids or contaminated personal items such as bedding and clothing. In those days, almost every family had more than one person sleeping in the same bed. Families had a lot of children and often three or four of them slept together. Unfortunately, until people were informed of the dangers, this was one of the primary ways of getting smallpox infection.

Again, using the same dipper for drinking easily spread body fluids; that is, saliva. Prolonged contact was another avenue the disease took. For example, kids playing contact sports at school or on the playground.

The death rate of smallpox was high, often as much at thirty percent of those contracting the disease. The disease had another bad side effect in that it often caused severe scarring on those who survived.

Pneumonia is the great mimicker. It is often disguised as cold or flu, and the person may not realize he or she has it. Even today, people can have it and not know it. It is still the sixth leading cause of death in the United States. It can be caused by either bacteria or virus and in rare cases, by fungi. A person will usually have fever, chills, coughing and chest pain. I became infected with pneumonia when I was one year old. My dad walked through several inches of snow to Amos Grant's house and asked him to take me to Robbinsville to old Doc Crawford. Mom said that the doctor gave me a red liquid in a small bottle. After a few hours, my pneumonia began to clear up. Even so, scarring of my left lung still shows up on an x-ray.

Prior to 1950, chokecherry was used as a folk medicine and by doctors to treat pneumonia along with a number of other ailments. Lewis and Clark documented they used it to treat cramps and fever. Its beneficial effects on the respiratory system were well known. People also made poultices of turpentine and lard and rubbed it on the chest. They also used this for colds and flu and had no real way of knowing which of the three diseases the sick person had.

In the early 1900's, whooping cough was one of

the major causes of death in young children. It is a highly infectious disease of the respiratory system. After the disease progressed, children coughed so hard that they whooped, thus the name. Respiratory arrest was the usual cause of death. A tea made from thyme was often used to reduce both the intensity and frequency of the coughing. Belladonna was used occasionally and met with some success in saving lives. This herb can be very poisonous when used in the wrong amount. Its alternate name is "deadly nightshade." Given the nature of the disease, people considered its use worth the risk.

Polio was another childhood disease that struck with epidemic proportions in the United States beginning in 1918. Once contracted, the disease was incurable. There were some epidemics in the United States almost every year after that. The disease actually decreased for some time and then came back with a vengeance after World War II. In the early fifties, quarantines were common place. There were really no remedies except to treat pain, use ventilators for those who had difficulty breathing and to treat secondary infections with antibiotics. About 25% of the children who contracted the disease died, and another 25% were crippled for life.

I remember well the quarantines where I lived at the time. Children were told not to associate with other children with whom they had not been in regular contact with prior to the quarantine. Four of us kids played monopoly for days on end.

In 1952 Dr. Jonas Salk developed the polio vaccine and by 1955, inoculations nationwide defeated the disease. The disease still lurks today, and there is no cure for it. The Salk vaccine is still the only clear-cut preventative measure. Most people don't realize that if vaccinations for these diseases were stopped nationwide, all of them would return with a vengeance.

Medical Superstitions

By and large, medical superstitions evolved out of mankind's ignorance about disease. Some of these can be traced as far back as Roman and Greek culture. In the main, most of them were carried to the Appalachians by immigrants from Europe, especially England, Scotland and Ireland. As recently as 1880, doctors often recommended superstitious methods in the absence of any medical remedy. Some of these superstitions were interwoven with religion. It's easy with today's modern medicine to ridicule those practices. Be that as it may, anyone who thinks they have gone away completely is misinformed. For example, it is not unusual for patients to have misgivings or even refuse to be placed in a hospital room that is numbered thirteen. Many people still believe that specific diseases were sent on certain persons by God because they committed some type of sin.

Almost all of us in the Appalachians can recount

stories by our parents and grandparents regarding medical remedies based on superstition. One of the most common was the belief that a knife placed under the mattress or an ax under the bed of a woman in labor would cut (reduce) her pain. Strangely, if the woman actually believed it, there is evidence that it probably helped to some degree. A person who was concerned about thinning hair would rub buttermilk on it. Another was to rub cow manure into the hair around the thinning area. This was about as extreme as the practice of pouring warm urine into the ear for earache. In this case, what helped the earache was the warmth, not the urine. Any kind of warm liquid would have been just as effective.

If a child had asthma, the father would take him or her to a tree and make a mark on the tree at the top of the child's head. The father would bore a hole in the tree a few inches above the mark. After that, the child was not to go near the tree. As he or she grew in height, the asthma would begin to diminish, and when the child's height passed the height of the hole in the tree, the asthma would completely disappear. In most cases, childhood asthma did diminish with age thus lending credence to the superstition. Two other methods were to put a stick or an ax handle up the chimney or in the attic. Again, the child was not to see them.

There were probably ninety-nine remedies to remove warts. Only special people had the ability to remove these troublesome growths although no one could explain exactly why those particular people could do it, or for that matter, if they actually did. I know from experience that a friend of mine from Robbinsville told me that his dad could remove warts when he learned I had a large one on the underside of my thumb. I had actually tried two or three brands of wart removal crème to no avail. He convinced me to let his dad remove them. His dad placed his thumb on my wart, sat silently for a few seconds, and then told me it would go away. He instructed me not to touch it or look at it. I did the best I could to do as instructed even though I didn't believe him. In about two weeks, the wart fell off, and my hand healed over the spot. Would it have gone away anyway? I honestly don't know. I learned later that a lot of people in the Robbinsville area went to him to remove their warts, and he was reputed to have a high degree of success. He did not charge for his service. He told me that taking money would interfere with the cure.

Eating raw potatoes was supposed to kill worms. Other remedies were to eat ginger root or garlic. Another was to mix ground pumpkin seeds, honey and water and drink the potion three or four times per day.

I have heard of people who could draw fire out of a burn. Nita said that her Grandma Cordie believed she could do it. People would often get boils on their skin. The old folks called them "risins." I have also heard them called "biles." It is now known that they were most often caused by infrequent bathing or wearing soiled clothing for several days. They believed the boils were caused by bad blood. They would take laxatives such as Black Draught or Caster Oil to cleanse the blood. This remedy certainly cleansed the bowels. Putting a piece of fatback or lard on the boils was used to draw them out so they could be pricked or pinched without damaging the skin.

Another common belief was that the blood was either too thick or too thin. It was common knowledge among mountain folk that the blood thickened in the winter. So when spring came, they would drink sassafras tea each morning for several days. This supposedly thinned the blood and alleviated all manner of conditions such as sluggish bowels, caused the kidney and bladder to function better and kicked the person out of the winter doldrums. People who were anemic, lacked energy or were generally lethargic were said to have thin blood. They were given blackstrap molasses, garlic and several other herbal remedies. While some of these remedies were actually helpful for some maladies, both thick and thin blood per se was usually a figment of the imagination.

Curative Love

U p to this point, it sounds like mountain medicine was simply administering herbal remedies to sick people or trying foolish cures that
didn't work. This is only partially true. In fact, it was
much more. Despite long hard hours and endless
days of drudgery, mountain people made time for their
sick. They treated the whole person by dispensing
herbal medications, enduring round the clock vigils by
sick beds and providing tender loving care. I know
from experience it was not unusual for a mother of
eight or ten children to sit up all night with a sick child
or aging parent. Often, several members of a family
would participate in care giving. One would prepare
and administer teas, powder, poultices or whatever it
took to make the sick person more comfortable. Other
members would cook, boil water, and wash bed
clothes and all the other general duties it took to look
after a sick person.

All the duties that are now performed by doctors,

nurses, and other health professionals were performed by family members. When I had scarlet fever at age eight, Mom and Dad took turns sitting up all night with me. I don't remember if Dad had a job at the time, but if he did, I'm sure he went to work the next day. Fortunately, I got well; many others didn't. Neighbors would often help, and church members would come by with food and other creature comforts they could afford. Prayer vigils were held for the very sick and terminally ill.

Often, someone would sit by the sick bed and read from the Bible which they called the Good Book. A Bible might be found any place in the home, but it was very unusual to find one with dust on it. Sometimes the sick person got well, and sometimes they didn't. If the person got well, it was God's will. If the person died, it was still God's will. They accepted their fate and buried their dead. Sometimes, the tombstone was just a flat stone stuck in the ground at the end of the grave. As long as they lived, they all knew which stone belonged to whom. It never occurred to them their descendents wouldn't know which stones marked the burial of their ancestors.

Through toil and troubles, their faith got them through the hard times, and they were thankful for the good times. They lived, loved and struggled. They doctored with the best they had at their particular time in history. Our kids will never know the hardships they suffered, and that's a good thing. Today, we take our loved ones to antiseptic hospitals with specialized care. Certainly, we have it better than our grandparents did. Even so, the hospitals don't provide one of the major elements in caring for the sick, although they like to pretend they do. That element is round-the-clock personalized love. Our grandparents understood that part of mountain medicine. They gave their love to their sick unconditionally, and because of them, we are here to enjoy a better life than they had. We should be thankful every day they cared and gave their best to the practice of mountain medicine.

CHAPTER FOUR
Roaming the Appalachians

Hole in the Box

As I drove north on Highway 36 in West Virginia, I enjoyed the natural beauty of the surrounding countryside. Bubbling brooks, sparkling waterfalls and misty mountains enthralled me so much that it took a couple of minutes for me to realize that a hissing sound emanated from under the hood of my truck. I came to a sharp curve and saw a winding road meandering off through the forest. I decided to take it. The "check engine light" came on just as I pulled into an old dilapidated service station. The bearded attendant with his hat on backwards told me I needed a new thermostat. The bad news was he didn't have one that would fit my truck. He could order it and a delivery van would drop it off the next morning. "Where am I?" I asked.

The guy grinned sheepishly. "You're in Looneyville," he said.

"Are things that bad around here?" I asked.

"I'm serious," he said. "That's the name of our community, and it's a good place to live."

Fearing I might have offended him, I changed the subject. "I'll have to sleep in my truck tonight. Okay if I leave it here?"

"You can," he said, "but my cousin, Ida Mae, boards people sometimes. You'd get a couple of meals thrown in, too."

"Fine with me," I said, "let's call her."

As it turned out, Ida Mae was a nice looking woman, late thirties and a grass widow. She was considered upper crust around Looneyville because she owned a doublewide. After a good country supper of fried potatoes, pinto beans and cornbread, Ida Mae asked me if I wanted to go to church with her.

I said I would, figuring I couldn't get into too much trouble at church. Being a rather versatile fellow, I never bothered to ask about her denomination. There were about a dozen cars and pickups in front when we arrived.

"Come on in," Ida Mae said, "and I'll introduce you to Brother Turner."

Brother Turner hugged Ida Mae and kissed her on the cheek, a little too friendly, I thought, but then, it wasn't my affair. He shook my hand and his eyes had a vacant stare that reminded me of an ex-con I once knew.

"Okay," Ida Mae said, "let's go up and demonstrate our faith."

I followed along, wondering what she meant. Two people were ahead of us and each of them stuck their right hand through a hole in a box and then pulled it out. They stepped away and Ida Mae and I stepped up. "I'll go first," she said.

I couldn't help but notice she was trembling when she put her hand in. She removed her hand, turned to me and said, "It's your turn."

"What's in that box?" I asked.

"You mean you don't know," she replied.

"I ain't got a clue," I said, "but I've got my suspicions."

Just then Brother Turner walked up. "You must demonstrate your faith, my friend, if you wish to attend our service."

Now I knew, but I asked him anyway just to be difficult. He reached deep into the box and pulled out the ugliest timber rattler I'd ever seen. He held it up in the air with both hands and then dropped it back through the hole in the box.

"See, Brother," he said, "if you have faith, he won't bite you."

"I don't think you understand, Brother Turner," I said. "My old Baptist Daddy told me that the only good rattlesnake is a dead rattlesnake, and I've made a practice of taking his advice."

By this time, all the church members had gathered around. "Brothers and Sisters, we have a non-believer in our midst," Brother Turner yelled out. "What're we gonna do about it?"

A woman in the back hollered out, "Make him handle the snake."

Whereupon three men grabbed me and started dragging me toward the box. Well, as it turned out, the Lord didn't give me faith to handle the snake but he gave me strength to resist. By the time we reached the box, ten men couldn't have made me stick my hand in it. I broke free and headed toward the front door. At least a dozen people blocked my path. I turned and ran toward the back, not knowing if there was another door or not. My pursuers were hot on my heels. Unbeknownst to me, there were several boxes of snakes on a table behind the pulpit. As two men came at me, I accidently bumped into the table. It turned over and the boxes went flying. Suddenly, rattlesnakes were crawling all over the floor.

The faithful flock suddenly became unfaithful. Apparently, they remembered the passage in Genesis about a snake bruising a man's heel. They all headed for the door in a hurry. A large lady who weighed in at about 250 pounds won the twenty yard dash followed closely by Brother Turner. I was reminded of my old high school days when Gary Owens ran interference for Joe Temple in a football game against Hickory. Several other people jerked the windows open and climbed out that way. It quickly dawned on me that since nobody headed for the back, there wasn't a door in the back. In less than two minutes, there wasn't anybody left in the church but me and the rattlesnakes. I grabbed a broom standing in the rear corner and jumped up on a table. After a few minutes, I saw heads staring in the windows. I looked down the aisle, and it was empty. All the snakes had crawled for cover. I put the broom down and walked slowly toward the front door. I reached it without incident and walked out.

Several people milling around outside began to

clap. "Okay, folks, you may resume your service," I said, "but unless your faith has returned, I recommend that you look in the pew before you sit down. Meanwhile, I'll just wait in Sister Ida Mae's car."

I got in and locked both doors. It took me a minute to realize that Ida Mae had already hidden in the back. She handed her car keys across the seat. I cranked her car and backed it up to turn around. In the rear view mirror, I saw Brother Turner come out from behind a big tree. I romped down on the accelerator and threw dust and gravel everywhere. Ida Mae told me later that she didn't realize her car would go from zero to sixty in three seconds.

The Good Parts of the Hog

I met Wilma Jean just east of Pine Knot, Kentucky. She had pulled her Gremlin off on the shoulder of the road because she had a flat tire. Trying to be a Good Samaritan, I pulled off about fifty yards ahead and walked back to help.

"Oh, thank goodness," she said, "I thought I'd have to spend the night in the back seat of my car." She gave me her best smile minus a couple of teeth.

I stooped down and looked at her tire. I was surprised it ever held air in the first place. The other three tires looked a little better, but not much.

"Do you have a jack?" I asked.

"Fraid not," she said.

"I'll go get the jack out of my car and see if it'll work."

"Won't do no good," she said. "Ain't nuttin' open fur fifty miles. Today's Saturday. All the local guys close up and go to the races."

"You mean they just lock their door and go?"

"Yep, they shore do."

"Do you want me to give you a lift?" I asked.

"Thought you'd never ask," she said.

We walked toward my car. She opened the door and jumped in, slamming the door hard enough to turn the car over.

"Oops, sorry," she said. "I forgot you have one of them new-fangled cars."

"It's seven years old," I said.

"I reckon, but hit's got new tars on it."

"I don't know any of these roads around here," I said. "There's a big traffic jam on I-75 and I'm trying to find my way around it. I missed my turnoff back there somewhere, and now, I don't have a clue where I am."

"That's okay," she said. "I can find my way round here in the dark with one eye shut. I used to ride with my daddy to haul his 'shine down to Oneida."

"Where's your daddy now?" I asked.

"He's in the pen over ta' Pine Knot," she said.

"Got caught with a big load," I guessed.

"Yeah, he outrun about a dozen cops, but one of'm got close enough to get his license number. They stormed the house at 3:00 in the morning. Like'ta scared my britches off."

After about ten turnoffs, I figured I'd never find my way back to the interstate, especially after dark.

"Turn off here," she said.

Suddenly, I smelled something rank. "What's that smell?" I asked.

"You must be smellin' the hog pens," she said.

Just then, I heard the hogs grunting.

"How many hogs you got?" I asked.

"Not many," she said. "I don't keep as many as Daddy did seeing as how I'm here by myself."

"Your mom dead?" I asked gently.

"Nah, she ran off with a holiness preacher from over Winfield way."

I pulled up into the yard. The hog pen was about twenty feet from the porch. I counted ten hogs including two sows that had at least ten piglets each. "Why don't you put the pens further away from the house?" I asked.

"You're pulling my leg, ain't ya? You don't really think I wanna lug them slop buckets way out in the field, do yah?"

"Makes sense," I said and dropped the subject.

"You know," she said, "hits gonna be dark right shortly. Do you think you can find your way back to the interstate?"

"I don't know," I said, "but I've got to try."

"You could spend the night here if you like, but I can tell by the way you wrinkle your nose you don't wanna sleep this close to my piggies. The barn's up the gulch there. There's hay in the loft. I can give you a couple quilts and a piller."

"That's okay," I said. "I've got a sleeping bag in the trunk of my car."

"Want some ham hocks and black-eyed peas before you turn in?" As my stomach lurched, I wondered what she did with the good parts of the hog.

"I had a late lunch down the road," I said. "Suit yourself," she said, "I'll wake you in the morning."

The barn didn't look like it had been used for

years, but there was plenty of dry hay in the loft. I rolled out my sleeping bag and listened to night sounds for a while. Suddenly, I heard footsteps coming across the barn floor.

"Ya all right up there?" Wilma Jean called from down below. Then I heard her climbing the steps. She sat down in the hay about ten feet away. "Wanna talk awhile?" she asked.

"Sure, why not," I replied.

Despite her lack of education, I quickly learned she was quite wise for her age, and she'd certainly had a hard life. She'd been living alone since she was fourteen. She sold her hogs for money to live on. She had an uncle close by who helped her out from time-to-time.

After about an hour, she yawned and stretched. "Guess I'll turn in," she said. She was gone as quickly as she arrived.

I drifted off to sleep.

I awoke to the sound of heavy rain on the barn roof. I'd been sleeping on my right side. As I listened to the rain, I became conscious of a warm body close to my back. I froze instantly. It appeared that Wilma Jean had moved in with me. I could hear gentle snoring. I lay perfectly still trying to decide how to handle the situation. I had to move, but how. My elbows were against a wall so the only way to get out was to crawl over her. Very carefully, I turned over. Before I figured out what was happening, a long wet tongue slurped me in the face. I sat up instantly, ready to fight. A huge bolt of lightning streaked across the sky, and I realized that my sleeping companion was a big

German shepherd dog. After both of us calmed down, we went back to sleep.

When next I awoke, the sun shone across the hay. My sleeping companion was gone and so was Wilma Jean. There was a note nailed to a porch post.

"I left ya some breakfust on the table," it read. Since I really hadn't eaten since the previous noon, I decided to go in and see what she had left for me. Surprisingly, I could barely smell the hog pens inside with the door closed. The house was clean enough to pass a military inspection. Right in the middle of an old worn dining table sat a plate loaded with country ham and boiled eggs. Another note told me where to find warm biscuits. I ate enough for three people. She hadn't returned by the time I finished. I figured the dog must have gone with her. I left two twenties on the table and wrote a note on top of her note.

"Buy yourself a new tire," I said.

I hit the road, spending two hours admiring the beauty in Daniel Boone National Forest. I had my oil changed at Wal-Mart in Williamsburg. I took my lunch bag out back and found a place to sit. As I munched on two delicious country ham biscuits from my breakfast plate, I finally understood what Wilma Jean did with the good parts of the hog.

Frog Legs a la Mississippi

It was June 20, 2008, and I was on the way home from Branson, Missouri. I hadn't eaten anything since breakfast. About halfway between Cairo, Illinois and Wickliffe, Kentucky, I saw a sign that read, "All the frog legs you can eat, $6.95." It was about six p.m. and I was famished.

I pulled into a parking space next to a newly painted sign that proclaimed, "Wagon Wheel Restaurant, Under New Management." I decided to look over the food bar before I ordered. Everything looked fresh and delicious. There in front of my eyes set a big pan of frog legs cooked to perfection. I picked up a plate, loaded it with six legs, fried potatoes and slaw. While the waitress went to fetch my coffee, I tried the legs and they were delicious. They really did taste like chicken, only much better.

The waitress came over and chatted with me while I consumed another half-dozen.

I asked where they got the frog legs.

"My twin brothers catch them," she said.

Somehow I mentioned I would like to go frog gigging someday.

She disappeared into the kitchen. While I munched on another leg, a genuine redneck showed up at my table. "Sis told me you'd like to go frog gigging," he said.

"I would," I replied, not knowing what was coming next.

"Me and my brother are going down Cane Creek tonight. Wanna come along?"

"Sure," I said, "but I don't know much about it."

"You don't need to," he said. "We be experts. Are you driving that big pickup out there?"

"I am," I said.

"Hit'll be dark in about an hour," he said. "How about if we stick our punt (boat) in the back and you drive?"

I couldn't help but notice that he spit tobacco in a tin can every couple minutes.

"The punt's out back. Just come out there when yer finished."

I took one last pass at the bar and picked up another half-dozen legs, skipping the sides. Going up to the register to pay, I offered to pay double.

"Oh no," the lady said. "Your supper's on the house if you're going frog gigging with my boys."

I drove around back where the twin rednecks were waiting, and introduced myself. The first twin shook my hand. "I'm Elmer," he said.

The other twin did the same. "I'm Elmer," he said.

"Now wait a minute," I said. "You can't both be Elmer."

"Are too," he said.

"You guys planning on being comedians all night?" I asked.

The first Elmer pulled out his well-worn wallet and showed me his Kentucky driver's license. It read, 'Elmer Charles Bennett.'

The other one pulled his out. It read, 'Charles Elmer Bennett.'

"So why isn't one of you called Charles?" I asked.

"Neither one of us likes that name," Elmer said.

"I'm surprised you weren't named Darryl and Darryl" I said.

"Dad couldn't spell it," Elmer said with a straight face. They went around the side and came back carrying the punt. It was about sixteen feet long.

"That thing's too long to go in my truck," I said.

They opened two latches in the middle and suddenly there were two eight-foot halves. We loaded them in the back along with three frog gigs, two head lamps and a long flashlight. Following Elmer's directions, I drove to Cane Creek which took about ten minutes.

Elmer and Elmer hooked the punt together and walked it to the creek. I carried the gigs and the lights. Elmer walked around a little bit and finally cut off two cane poles about ten feet long.

"Okay," Elmer said to me. "We'll set at each end and you set in the middle. You stay ready to blind the frogs with yer light." He reached into his pocket and handed me an ancient revolver.

"What's that for?" I asked. "Hit's for the cotton-mouths," he said. "They coil up in the trees and drop down sometimes."

"Just great," I said. They poled us out into the creek and then moved slowly along. They strapped their headlamps on and turned them on. In about two minutes, Elmer said, "There's one. Shine your light on him, Roy."

"I don't see anything," I said. Elmer pointed his light in the direction he wanted me to look. Suddenly, I saw two eyes gleaming in the dark. I pointed the light at them. Elmer and Elmer slowly poled the punt toward the eyes. Elmer in the front threw his gig and dead centered the frog. They poled up to it and picked it up. Elmer in the back stuffed the frog into a canvas sack.

Elmer and Elmer continued to pole the boat along. They passed the tin can back and forth by my nose and spit tobacco in it.

"Why don't you guys spit over the side?" I asked.

"Can't do that," Elmer said. "The frogs eat it. Mom claims it makes the legs taste bad."

"I thought that tenth leg I ate tonight tasted a little funny," I said, trying to play along with the joke. Any reasonable person would have known they were pulling my leg but I decided they were serious. Their mom was probably pulling their legs.

In about three hours, they had stuffed over fifty frogs in the sack. I began hearing a loud sound like lots of water running. "What's that noise," I asked.

"That's old Miss," Elmer said. "Ya see that big tree way yonder?"

I squinted in the moonlight. "I do."

"We can't pass that or we'll be swept all the way down yonder to New Orleans," Elmer said.

Suddenly Elmer in the front said, "Gosh almighty, look at that." A snake about four feet long was hanging from a limb. They started backing the punt up but it was too late. It dropped in the boat at my feet. I shined the light on it. It had two big fangs and a mouth lined with cotton. I jerked the pistol out of my belt, fired at the snake and missed. I pulled the trigger again and the gun jammed. Doing the next best thing, I jumped out of the boat, leaving Elmer and Elmer to deal with the snake.

As the punt drifted away, I could see them punching at it with their cane poles. Finally, they managed to get it overboard. "Gosh almighty," I heard Elmer in the front say, "The boats leaking."

"Tain't no wonder," Elmer in the back said. "That feller shot a hole in the bottom."

Now, I could barely see the punt in the moonlight. Finally, it drifted out of sight in the mist.

"Now what," I thought. I still had the flashlight in my hand and the gun in the other. I shined the light around. I heard a car pass nearby. I made my way toward the noise. The water got shallower and I finally reached the road. I started walking in the direction where I thought I had parked my truck. "Oh my goodness," I thought, "how am I going to explain to Elmer and Elmer's mama that her sons drowned in the Mississippi?"

I finally reached my truck. Just as I started out, I saw a car coming. The driver pulled over and a woman stuck her head out the window. "Better be careful," she said. "We just saw a big alligator coming across the field back there."

"I didn't know there were any alligators in the Mississippi," I said.

"There is now," she said as they pulled away.

Curiosity got the best of me. I turned my truck in that direction and drove slowly along. Suddenly, I saw something coming across the field. I pulled over. It was Elmer and Elmer, carrying the punt on their heads. They were wet all over and covered with leaves, grass and twigs. Truth be told, they were a scary sight. "I thought you guys had drowned," I said.

"Not us," Elmer replied, "We can swim better'n the frogs."

We loaded the punt in the back. I pretended not to see the hole. I handed the gun to Elmer. "Better oil it," I said.

I drove them back to the Wagon Wheel. It was 5:00 a.m., and Mama Bennett was in the kitchen. Elmer and Elmer went to a table and began separating the legs from the frogs. When they finished, they counted the legs three times. Apparently, they had trouble counting that high. Mama Bennett set a big plate of biscuits and gravy in front of each of us. I had two helpings.

"Thanks a lot," I said. "I'd better hit the road."

"Hang around," Elmer said. "We'll do it again."

"Not on your life," I thought, but I said, "Better not, I promised my wife I'd be home tomorrow."

West Virginia Graduate Degree

I'd never dated a West Virginia girl before, probably because I'd heard so many jokes about them. And then I met Debbie Lou Douthit. She was a tall brunette with a master's degree in psychology.

"Nobody will poke fun at an attractive woman with that much education," I thought.

She lived in South Charleston which, just for the record, is northwest of Charleston. Apparently, the city fathers never owned a compass. I'd hate to explain that little anomaly to the tourists. I was driving along Maccorkle Avenue on our first date.

"Kathy Mattea was born in this town, wasn't she?" I cautiously remembered.

Debbie Lou pointed to our left. "Right over there in the hospital."

I slowed down to look. "You go to school with her?" I wondered.

"I did," she said, "We graduated together."

I pulled into Starbucks for coffee. As an afterthought, I asked, "You and Kathy ever sing together?"

She rolled her eyes. "Heavens no," she laughed. "My mamma used to say I couldn't carry a tune with a milk bucket over my head."

We waited for our coffee to cool. "I did send Kathy a couple of songs," she reflected. "She sent me a thank-you note, but she never used them as far as I know."

When I phoned to arrange for my second visit, Debbie Lou asked if I would mind a double date. So I thought, "I'll get to meet some of her friends."

As it turned out, her idea of a double date was to bring her best friend, Ester Gay, with us to the drive-in theatre; my treat, of course. Right off the bat, they had a popcorn eating contest at five bucks a box. At least, they had the good manners not to make me sit in the middle. Good thing, too. Over the noise of the movie, I heard Ester Gay chewing on something. Curious, I asked her what she was chewing on.

"It's Beech Nut," she stated.

My mouth was a little dry after eating all that popcorn, so I asked her to share. She handed it to me. It was a little dark in the car, but still, it didn't look like gum to me. Apparently, she could see my frown in the light of the movie.

"Shoot Roy," she grumbled, "if you don't like Beech Nut, I've got some Skoal in my purse."

As I got to know Debbie Lou a little better, I was amazed at the amount of garlic she ate. I finally worked up the nerve to ask her why she ate so much.

"It keeps vampires away," she pointed out.

"You're talking about the bats that live in caves

over in Coal Fork," I ventured.

"No way," she replied. "I'm talking about undead people with two big fangs that bite people on the neck."

At the end of a long pregnant pause, I decided to risk another question. "How do people become undead?"

"Well, duh," she proclaimed, "they die and then come back to life."

I mulled that over for a few seconds. Not satisfied, I continued. "So, how do they come back to life?"

She looked at me like I was an ignoramus. "They're possessed by the devil," she replied emphatically.

"And you obtained all this knowledge where?"

"I learned it from my grandmother."

"Did your grandmother actually see a vampire?"

"Of course not!"

"Don't tell me, let me guess; that's because she ate lots of garlic!"

"You're a fast learner for a guy who only has an undergraduate degree."

After about three months, she casually mentioned her ex-husband for the first time.

"Tell me about him," I coached gently.

"Well," she said, "he chewed tobacco, spent his spare time coon hunting, hung out with a bunch of trailer trash, drank Pabst Blue Ribbon for breakfast and burped in church."

She had my attention. "I assume that's why you divorced him."

"No," she said, "I divorced him because he kept

going to the Parkersburg Drive-in Theatre with his first cousin."

Somehow, I wasn't making the connection. "I gather he was a bad influence."

"No, he wasn't, she was! He was dating her behind my back." she seethed.

My next statement just slipped out. "Maybe, they were just kissing cousins."

She stared at me for several seconds. "Are you sure you have an undergraduate degree?"

I would have kept dating her but she had a medical problem I couldn't live with. She was allergic to soap. At first, I thought she might be French, so I asked her.

"Not that I know of," she said. "Mom and dad met at a family reunion in Bluefield."

I chewed on that for a few seconds. "So you're your own second cousin," I deadpanned.

"Third," she quickly replied. I decided to go for broke.

"Was your ex-husband your cousin?" I coaxed, keeping a straight face.

"No, dummy. He was my brother-in-law."

"You married your sister's husband?"

"Yeah, but I didn't know it; he lied to me."

"You didn't ask your sister if they had divorced," not believing what I'd heard.

"I didn't want to pry into her business."

"So they weren't divorced?"

"Bring your college diploma with you the next time you come up. I want to see it."

"Turn about's fair play," I advised. "I'll show you

mine if you'll show me yours."

She took me to her bedroom and pointed at the wall. Her diploma hung prominently in an expensive-looking frame. I walked over and stared at it. At the top, written in scrolled letters was, "BOL College," and directly under that in smaller letters, "An extension of West Virginia State University."

"Don't tell me; let me guess," I sniggered. "BOL stands for Bubba's On Line Graduate School."

"Don't be a smarty pants. It stands for Bolivar, the town where the University Graduate School is located."

On the way home, I decided to drive through Bolivar. I knew it was next door to Harper's Ferry. I pulled up beside two men getting ready to cross the street. "You guys know where the graduate school is?"

When they stopped laughing, the taller one said, "Go down the street to the Bolivar Times. Ask for Billy Bob Bixby."

Five minutes later, I walked into the newspaper office. Billy Bob greeted me with a big smile.

"You come in for a diploma?" he guessed. I looked around. The walls were lined with examples of graduate diplomas. I figured I might as well join the fun.

"You got a PhD in Physics?" I inquired.

"Doctoral diplomas are five dollars more," he advised.

"I can handle it," I said.

In less than ten minutes he handed me a tube containing my literary document. On my way out of town, I turned on the radio. Emerald Rose was belting out their latest hit song, "Never Underestimate a Woman." I glanced over at my brand-new diploma and wondered if Debbie Lou had been sending songs to them.

Big Bone Lick

I had spent the night sleeping in the back of my truck in Big Bone Lick State Park in northern Kentucky. As was my habit on my walkabouts, I called Nita early in the morning to let her know where I was.

"You're pulling my leg," she said. "There's no such place."

I did occasionally pull her leg so it took a little convincing. "Look it up on Google," I said. "A lick is a ridge running out from a mountain. The big bone refers to mammoth and mastodon bones that have been found here."

I waited while she looked it up. "Well, I'll be darned," she said. "There really is such a place."

After I hung up the phone, my stomach started gnawing on my belt buckle. I decided to look for a place to eat.

Tthe attendant in the tourist center said the nearest place was a small diner in Rabbit Hash. I headed out and in a few minutes rounded the curve and saw two buildings, one on each side of the road. Geraldine's Diner was on the right and the Rabbit Hash General Store was on the left. The diner was open; the store wasn't. Geraldine met me at the door and told me to take my choice of seats. I took the back booth. "You want bacon and eggs or ham and eggs?" she asked.

I answered her question with a question. "You got any biscuits and gravy?"

Her eyes twinkled. "You're from somewhere in the South," she said. "I don't serve them because these tourists don't want them, but I'll tell you what. I've got biscuits and I can whip up some gravy in a few minutes if you don't mind waiting."

I didn't mind, so I waited. After about five minutes, two girls came in, obviously twins. One of them had on a red T-shirt and a blue skirt. The other one had on a blue T-shirt and a red skirt. They were spitting images of Geraldine except they were much younger. Obviously, the Lord had blessed them four times instead of twice. Their skirts were too long for a nudist colony and too short for a church picnic. They went into the kitchen, and I went back to reading the Grit I had found on the counter.

Shortly, Geraldine brought out my biscuits and gravy with hash browns and crispy bacon. She blushed when I told her she was the best cook in Kentucky.

There were no other customers in the diner so Geraldine came out and joined me. Soon the twins also came out. Geraldine introduced them as Bobbie and Billie.

"They're seventeen going on thirty," she said.

"No argument there," I replied.

Toward the end of the meal, she asked me what I was going to do with the rest of my day.

"I'm going back over to Big Bone and look the place over.

"Want some company?" she asked.

"Sure," I said, "but won't you have to close the diner?"

"I'm not talking about me," she said, "I meant the girls. They know Big Bone like the back of their hands, and it'll get them out of the diner for a while."

It was my turn to blush. I couldn't figure a way out so I agreed. Outside, both girls piled into the front seat with me. I felt like I was escorting models from Victoria's Secret. I put the truck in gear and headed back to the park. It was an effort to keep my eyes on the road but I managed. While I drove, they gave me a rundown on the history of the park.

After touring the museum, we headed out to the boardwalk and around the marsh bog. The mastodon and mammoth displays were fascinating. We enjoyed the beauty of the lake and then took a non-tourist trail that led up the slope of Big Bone Lick. When we got to the bottom of the slope, Bobbie suggested that since they were familiar with the trail, they should go up first.

"I'll go first if you don't mind," I said.

"Why?" she asked.

"It's better for my blood pressure," I said.

They looked mystified but said nothing. A little way up the trail, I heard them giggling. Apparently, they finally figured out what I meant.

Later, we decided to wander around the campground. At one point, the trail narrowed and they had to walk in front. A skunk decided to cross just in front of us. I thought they were nocturnal, but nobody had told this one. We vamoosed in a hurry. We walked back to the tourist center and to get some snacks from the vending machines. Every guy we passed stared at us.

"Do you think all these guys are staring at me?" I asked.

Their response was to giggle. I bought two moon pies, a pack of cheese crackers and a coffee. They each asked for a fruit bar and a diet drink. "You're not eating much," I said.

"We have to watch our figures," Bobbie informed me.

"Apparently everybody else does too," I said.

We found a picnic table next to a couple. I noticed that the wife was petite and the husband could pass for a gorilla. We hadn't been seated long when an unkempt fellow with a two day growth of beard and a missing front tooth sidled up.

"Hi girls," he said. "Where'd you find the old guy?"

"Get lost, Gomer," Bobbie said.

"Yeah, Goober, take a long walk on a short pier," Billie said.

"Come on, girls," Bubba said, "Stop playing hard to get."

"The ladies asked you to get lost," I said. "I think you should take their advice."

With the meanest look he could muster, he said, "Buzz off Grandpa."

Just as I eased my pepper spray out of its case, the gorilla stood up. He looked bigger standing up than he did sitting down.

"My nieces asked you to leave," he said. "You've got thirty seconds before I break your arm in three places."

Suddenly, Bubba looked plain scared. He turned, walked away and never looked back

"Thanks," I said. "I was about ten seconds away from spraying him in the snoot."

"I saw that," he replied, "so I decided you wouldn't turn down a little help."

His wife spoke for the first time. "Robbie's an amateur wrestler," she said proudly.

"What's your ring name? I asked.

"Barn Burner," he replied with a big grin.

"I hope I get to see you wrestle sometime," I said.

We finished our snack, and I drove the girls back to Geraldine's diner. We all trooped into the kitchen. Geraldine was standing at the grill. "You need to lock these two up until they're twenty-one," I said.

"No argument there," she replied.

Avalance

I worked at the resistor plant in Boone from 1974 to 1982. This meant driving a one hundred mile round trip every day unless I stayed in my tiny apartment I had rented for bad weather days. Believe me, there were plenty of those. One way or another, I went home every weekend for seven years. On several occasions, I drove the fifty miles from Boone to Morganton through the snow with a set of chains on my rear tires. Two trips that distance would wear out a set of chains.

In the spring of 1980, we had more rain than usual and the first week of May it rained nonstop for about five days and finally stopped on Friday morning. As usual, I headed out on Friday afternoon. Everything went fine for a few miles.

About a mile down the mountain below Blowing Rock, I came upon a woman beside the road who obviously had trouble with her car. I pulled up behind her and got out to see if she needed help. She was an

African-American woman who appeared to be about my age. I could see that she was trembling so I knew something had scared her. Also, she was afraid to roll down the window because I was a stranger, and she was on a strange road. She finally rolled down the window a couple of inches so I could talk to her. She told me that she was afraid of driving on the mountain and had pulled over because of her nerves. I talked to her for several minutes until she calmed down.

Finally, I told her I would get back on the road and drive slowly. That way, she could follow behind me. I mentioned to her to be careful about riding her brakes because they would overheat, and that I would pull over every other mile, so she could cool them.

I drove a straight shift at the time, and I knew to just downgear so I wouldn't have to ride my brakes. She didn't have that privilege because her car had an automatic transmission. When I could find a place to pull over, we stopped and chatted while her brakes cooled. By the third stop I had gotten to know her quite well. By the fourth stop, it had started raining again and within five minutes it turned into a deluge. This made her even more afraid so we sat and waited until it slacked off again.

At about a mile above the bottom of the mountain, we passed a section that had cliffs on the upper side of the road. Suddenly, I heard a loud crack of some undetermined origin. It sounded like God had snapped a huge oak tree in the middle. Operating on reflex, I stomped down on the accelerator. The car sped up quickly because I was driving downhill. I glanced in my rearview mirror and saw a wall of boulders come down behind me. I pulled over a couple of hundred yards down the road and got out of the car. An avalanche had completely covered both sides of the road and I could still hear rocks rolling down the mountain. I realized if I hadn't floorboarded it, I would have been under that mountain of rocks. Then, it hit me that my companion was buried under a conglomeration of giant boulders.

As I dashed back up the road to see, it dawned on me that if she really were buried, there would be nothing I could do. I forced myself to wait until I was sure that rocks had stopped falling. While I waited, it started pouring rain again. I went back to my car, got my umbrella and started back. This time, I began the slow process of climbing over the rocks. As I crossed the top of the pile, I was flabbergasted to see her car sitting in an open space between two rock slides. As I climbed down, I saw her front bumper was about two feet from a rock twice as big as her car. I made my way around to the driver's side. She sat there with her hands still frozen on the steering wheel. I started banging on her window to get her attention. Finally, she looked at me.

"Vanessa," I said, roll down the window." I had to repeat myself five or six times. Fortunately, the door was unlocked, and I opened it. "Come on lady," I said, "let's get you out of here."

She nodded but didn't move. I reached over and shook her by the shoulder. "Come on, let's go," I said.

"I can't get out," she said. "I've wet the seat."

"That doesn't matter," I said. "We've got to get out of here before the mountain comes down again."

She nodded and I pulled on her enough to get her started. Just as I got her out of the car, a head popped up on the upper side of the upper rock pile. "Are you okay?" A man called out.

"I think so," I said. "Can you help me get her to my car?"

"I'll be happy too," he said. "Where is your car?"

"Just below the rock pile," I said.

"Is anyone buried under these rocks?" he asked.

"Not unless they are between this car and yours," I said.

"I don't think anyone was behind me," Vanessa said.

I could see that she was coming out of her shock. "Do you think we can climb over without this man's help?"

"I think so," she said.

"Sir," I said. "We certainly appreciate your help, but you'd better get back up to your car before another slide comes down the mountain."

He turned back and climbed over while we went downhill over the lower rock pile. By the time we got across, several cars were stopped on the lower side.

Two women were in the first car below me and a couple behind them. After some discussion, the two women volunteered to take Vanessa home.

"What should I do about my car?" she asked.

"Will one of you ladies help her call the Sheriff's Department?" I asked.

"Yes," they said. "We'll be happy to."

Vanessa thanked me several times before she got in their car. As I continued on down the mountain, I met two Sheriff's cars coming up with lights flashing. Bad news travels fast.

I'm sure that Vanessa's guardian angel and mine were working together that rainy day. I'm still amazed that we weren't both killed. As far as I know, the mountain didn't slide any more. The road was closed for about a month. During that time, I had to drive up Highway 181 through Jonas Ridge to get to work. After the road opened back up, I drove down that mountain for another two years. Every time I passed that section of road, I would look up the mountainside and listen for any unusual noise. As far as I know, that area never had another rock slide.

Flower-Loving Slave Driver

A few year's ago, I signed up for a class called "Understanding Wildflowers" at Western Piedmont Community College in Morganton. The course was taught by one of the college teachers, a delightful woman named Ruby Pharr. Now, Ruby has forgotten more about wildflowers than I'll ever know. A required part of the course was an overnight field trip to study flowers in their natural habitats. Anyone who didn't take their flowers seriously was doomed to failure. Some of the students were taking the class for credit, but I was doing it for enjoyment, or so I thought. Ruby's husband, Walter, a plant manager in Shelby, always went along quite simply because Ruby needed a gofer.

Ruby served meals on this trip as part of the tuition. They were the best low fat, healthy meals I've ever eaten. Walter was truly a lucky man, and he knew it. I actually went on four of her trips, although repeats were generally not allowed. I accomplished this by brown-nosing. On this, the first trip, we stayed in a rustic cabin on Mr. Bell's property at Tuxedo, NC, which is near Hendersonville. We drove down a dirt road and parked as close to the cabin as we could. From there, we carried in our sleeping bags and all the food.

Ruby's meals were a mixture of fruits, nuts and vegetables. Everything had been prepared before she left home. We all ate heartily, and I helped clean up the dishes. This was my first effort at brown-nosing. There were twelve students in all, ranging in ages from eighteen to seventy; men and women from all walks of life. At least a half-dozen had dropped out before the field trip. After the meal, we sat around and got to know each other. I was into jogging at the time, and I decided to go, even though there were no bathing facilities at all. As I donned my shoes and shorts, a nurse asked if she could join me. Since she was young and attractive, I couldn't find a reason to say no. Also, if one falls and breaks a leg in the woods, it's not a bad idea to have a nurse along.

We took off down a logging road at a fast clip. We were both into long distance running. We ran close to an hour, down one logging road after another. Finally, we stopped, caught our breath and started back. After working our way along several roads, we realized we were lost. We continued walking until it started getting dark. We didn't have a clue where we were so we sat down to discuss the situation, and decided the best plan of action was to rake up a big pile of leaves to sleep on because it looked like we were going to spend the night in the woods. We did that and then sat with our backs against a tree trunk and told each other our life stories. We heard a noise and looked up. We saw headlights coming down the logging road. Mr. Bell, a robust man well into his eighties, pulled up in his jeep.

"I hate to ruin your night," he said, "but Mrs. Pharr drove up to the house and asked me to hunt you."

We were both glad to see him even though he teased us about getting lost on purpose. It was about eleven when we arrived back at the cabin. Ruby was waiting like an anxious mother.

"I've never lost anybody yet," she said, "but I thought you two were going to be the first."

Then she laced into us just like a mother would. Since we were the last to go to bed, we had the worst spots. I climbed up into a tiny room on the side of the cabin and the nurse spread her sleeping bag out on the dirt floor between two bunks. About midnight, it started raining. I had just gotten to sleep when I heard a ruckus in the cabin. Two people, a businessman and his secretary were having words. In a few moments, I heard someone climbing up the little ladder to my cramped quarters. The lady wanted to know if she could sleep behind me to get away from her boss. I grudgingly agreed, and she crawled over me to get into the back. In a few minutes, she was asleep. Unfortunately for me, she snored like a lumberjack. The rain on the tin roof would lull me to sleep, and her snoring would wake me up. Next morning, I suggested that she should have her adenoids removed.

At daybreak, it was still raining lightly. Ruby

started beating on something that sounded like a dinner triangle on a chuck wagon. Always in good cheer, she started preparing breakfast. After a delicious meal of hot pancakes with blueberries, walnuts and maple syrup, Ruby told everyone to get ready to move out. She had told us to bring raincoats, and now we understood why. Ruby walked through a hole in the underbrush, and we reluctantly followed. Despite our raincoats, we were soaked in a short time. The rain did not quell Ruby's good humor, and she found a variety of wildflowers. Walter would lie on the grass or in the leaves and hold the foliage aside while we photographed the flowers.

Ruby had strict rules about disturbing nature's bounty. Anybody who pulled a flower, plant or weed was subject to a severe tongue lashing. On and on we went through the wet forest. Wet clothing, wet shoes and eventually, wet tempers. Ruby showed no mercy. Nobody but she and Walter knew where we were. At about 1:00 p.m., we magically appeared at the cabin. We all sat around and shivered while Ruby prepared another of her world class lunches. As soon as we finished eating, the flower-loving slave driver drove us back into the woods. This time Ruby slowed the pace a little. At each flower, she would stop and give us the physical attributes, history, ecology, geographical habitat and relationship to other plants and animals. We learned about plant communities, forest reclamation, insect relationships, edible and poisonous plants and a whole host of plant variables.

Promptly at 6:00 p.m., Ruby called a halt to the torture. I think she realized that she was about an hour short of having a rebellion on her hands. Back in the vans, we warmed up and sang songs on the way home. Everybody promised to keep in touch which none of us did. I found out later that Mr. Bell hired the nurse as a counselor at his girl's camp. I wondered why the rascal never offered me a job, and then it occurred to me it was because I had skinny legs. I had about three hundred pictures of wildflowers, and 280 were pretty bad. About twenty turned out beautiful, and I used them to start a scrapbook. I probably signed up the second time for the same reason that marines re-enlist. The rewards of being tortured can be extremely gratifying. I think there's a name for that.

Man's Best Friend

Way back when, I worked as a department manager for Modular Research, a company headquartered in Montgomery, Alabama. Nilo Queen was president and CEO. He was one of those arrogant types who thought he was right up there next to God. Every Thursday evening, he held two meetings. I attended the first one and the second one was only for the stockholders. At that time, Nilo was pushing fifty.

One evening after the first meeting, he came out and told me to drive his gorgeous young wife home. From that point on, giving her a ride became a regular event. Despite the fact that I was driving Camille to her residence because he had ordered me to do so, Nilo got it in his paranoid head that she and I were having an affair. So on the following Friday morning, he ordered the personnel manager to fire me. I told him to tell Nilo that if I outlived him, I would desecrate his grave. It only took a week to find another job; but still, I had an urge to get even. I soon figured out that was illegal so I dropped the idea.

Thirty-five years came and went. One evening I was prowling on the internet and came across a rather lengthy article about Nilo's death. The article went on to detail all the great services the man had provided for the city and casually mentioned that he had left Camille an estate of 300 million dollars. Naturally, I couldn't help but feel sorry for her. The article also went on to detail the funeral service and the cemetery where he had been interred.

About a month later, I had business in Mobile. I had to go through Montgomery so I decided to look into Nilo's resting place. After all, I had a promise to keep. The cemetery was easy enough to find. It was entirely surrounded by a tall wrought-iron fence. Looking inside, I quickly realized there were no graves. The place was wall-to-wall mausoleums and the front gate was locked.

Directly across from the front gate was a large house. I knocked and when the owner came to the door. I asked if he knew when the cemetery was open. He looked at me like I'd lost it. "That's a private ceme-tery; the gate is never open. Which mausoleum are you interested in?"

When I told him, he laughed. "Old Nilo has the biggest mausoleum in the cemetery. It's pink marble and it's in the back. There's a separate entrance so a landscaping service can mow the grass and tend the shrubs and flowers. If you want to look at it through the fence, you can drive around to the back."

I did and behind the cemetery was a wooded

area. I found a place where I could park my truck so it wasn't in view of any house. The fence was tricky to climb but I managed. Nilo's mausoleum was surrounded by another wrought-iron fence inside the main cemetery. That fence wasn't as high as the outside fence but it was more ornate. And of course, it was easier to climb. The lawn inside Nilo's fence was perfectly manicured with elaborate flower beds in strategic locations. As I surveyed the opulence of the highly-crafted tomb, a scruffy-looking dog came out from behind it. Apparently, he had sneaked in while the landscapers were taking care of the grounds. He looked hungry so I gave him a granola bar that I had in my pocket. As he walked away, he cocked his leg and gave the corner of Nilo's tomb a small bath. "Now there's a dog I could learn to like," I said.

Much to my surprise, Nilo's mausoleum wasn't locked. When I entered, low lighting came on and funereal music started playing. The dog followed me in. The inside was as fancy as it was on the outside, if not more so. In one corner, a huge cut-glass vase rested on a green marble table. The beautiful flowers in the vase looked so real I had to touch them to make sure they were silk. Between the door and the table, three elaborately carved chairs waited for mourners. On the left wall, three expensive oil paintings showed Nilo at three different ages. On the opposite wall, a large plaque inlaid in gold detailed a long list of Nilo's achievements. The ceiling was painted with a mural that showed three Angels carrying Nilo up to heaven.

"Now there's an interesting piece of fiction," I said to the dog.

Against the back wall, three marble drawers were built into the tomb. Each drawer had gilded designs on the front with gold plated handles. Thinking Nilo would be in the top drawer, I pulled on the handle. It slid out effortlessly, but it was empty. The middle drawer had a variety of electronics which, I think, controlled the lighting, music and automatic sprinklers for the outside. As it turned out, Nilo's body was in the bottom drawer. I figured that was his wife's final vengeance.

There Nilo lay, looking just like his picture on the internet. Whoever embalmed him had done a masterful job. I stood and stared at the corpse for a few seconds and waxed philosophical. In death, a rich man is no greater than a poor man, I thought. I heard a noise outside. I peered out the door, but it was just a bird. Suddenly, I heard water splashing. I turned and looked at the dog.

"You are definitely man's best friend," I said, and petted him for his good job and closed the drawer with my shoe. Making sure he was following me; I went out and closed the door to the mausoleum. I carried him over the inside fence but I had to toss him over the outside fence. I thought he would go on his way, but he followed me to the truck. I rounded up two more granola bars, fed him those and put him in the back.

Upon arrival at my destination, I located a pet friendly motel. Next morning, I took him to a groomer. When I got him back, he was the best looking dog in Mobile, Alabama. On the way home, he rode up front in the passenger seat. After all, he had earned the privilege.

Since I already had two dogs, I gave my new pal to a friend who lives in Banner Elk. She lives alone and needed a good watch dog. About three months later, I called her.

"How's Avenger doing?" I asked.

"Oh, he's a great dog," she replied. "But I can't take him to a cemetery. He has no respect for the dead."

CHAPTER FIVE
Farmer's Helpers

Fair Dealings

W hen I was growing up in Nantahala, farm animals were part and parcel of everyone's livelihood. Today, people run farms with big tractors, combines, seeders, pickers and harvesters. A farmer can now harvest fifty acres of grain without getting out of his air-conditioned combine. But back then, farming was done with the use of animals. Oxen, mules, horses and milk cows were well cared for and kept in barns at night.

Chickens and ducks were kept for their eggs and meat, and geese were kept for their feathers to make pillows. Hogs were the main source of meat although a few beef cattle were kept by people like my Uncle John, General Owenby and Ervin Grant. A few people had sheep and goats, but they were in the minority. Dogs were kept for hunting, and cats were used to keep rats and mice out of the house, barn and out-buildings.

When men sat around Weaver Cochran's store,

the subject was usually about who had caught the most fish, had the best team of oxen, or the oldest mule. Coon hunting was one of their favorite sports, and the men bragged about their favorite dogs like they were family members. Of course, the dogs had colorful names like Old Blue, Stubby, Rattler, Hambone, and Wash Tub.

In general, men were noted for their fair dealings in farm and draft animals. If a man bought a cow from another, and it died soon after the sale, the buyer would usually be reimbursed. Children were sometimes given piglets or calves for Christmas or birthday presents as a way to teach them the responsibility of raising farm animals. Parents would often encourage their children to save their pennies for the purpose of buying a shoat or a heifer at a stock sale. The child would then feed and care for their charge until it was grown. Sometimes, the sale or slaughter of the animal would end in a heart-wrenching experience because the child had become so attached to it.

Children were taught to plow and harvest at an early age. A large family was the norm, and everyone pitched in to keep meat and vegetables on the table. I know of five Owenby generations before my father that had seven to twelve children per family. They were all farmers, well versed in the use of draft animals and livestock as a means of survival.

Oxen were noted for their strength and endurance. A good farmer put a lot of thought into matching his team. To work well together, they had to pull with about the same endurance and speed. They needed to be healthy, of the same breed and about the same size, and of course, they needed to be started young and trained together. An ox team was usually two steers, but not always. In the book of Judges, Samson told the Philistines if they hadn't plowed with his heifer, they wouldn't have guessed his riddle. Of course, he was talking about Delilah, but the comparison was an accurate analogy. Throughout history, a variety of breeds, mixtures and genders have been used as draft animals. Be that as it may, the best teams were made through selection and breeding.

If the proper choices were made, the team would be especially useful for pulling heavy loads. If a farmer had to clear a patch of new ground, his or his neighbor's ox team could pull the logs and stumps away from the desired plowing area. The team would lean forward and pull their load strong and steady. While they were slower than horses, they would still be pulling when horses tired out. Back in the pioneer days, oxen were the animals of choice when families moved. In Western movies, horses were always por-trayed as the animal of choice for covered wagons, but this was only partially true. Families would pack up their belongings on the largest wagons they could find and then hitch up one, two or sometimes three ox teams. The oxen would pull the wagons all day, eat grass off the land and continue on the next day. My Aunt Alcie told me that Great-Grandpa Porter used oxen when they moved from Gum Log, Georgia, to Nantahala in the late 1860's. They followed the dirt roads and wagon trails through Murphy, Andrews, and on to Briartown via the winding stairs. That must have been some trip. I'm sure his brothers and sisters came the same way.

The successful use of an ox team required a good yoke, and not just anybody could make one. A good yoke maker took his job seriously, and he put a lot of love and care into it. In larger farming states, professionals made most yokes, but in the Smoky Mountains, most farmers made their own or bartered with a neighbor who might happen to be more skilled. If properly care for, a good yoke would last for generations. Like anything else, those that were hardest to make would last the longest. Hickory, oak, maple and even chestnut were used, depending on experience and preference. It had to be made of wood, preferably without knots, that would not split easily because the ox team exerted a lot of pressure against the yoke. The edges had to be rounded sufficiently so they wouldn't cut into the animal's skin. If the ox hide was worn through, the animal wouldn't pull properly which meant the team was out of commission.

Oxen often balked like mules, but they weren't as smart so they didn't get away with it as much as mules did. It took a good manager to get a team to work together. The animals responded to their owner as part of the team. Someone else might not be able to get them to work very well. Oxen were known to be slow, but they pulled with a steady strength whereas a horse pulled with a jerking motion. Each animal had their advantages and disadvantages. In times of drought or bad weather, an ox could eat almost any kind of corn, grain or silage. An ox would eat moldy hay without complaint while a horse often wouldn't touch it because they have sensitive digestive systems. Part of this is because a horse only has one stomach and an ox has a stomach with four compartments, each serving a separate function.

Ox teams played an important role in Appalachian farming, and those of us who saw them worked remember them with fondness.

Bragging Rights

In early Nantahala days, everybody walked or rode a wagon. One wonders why people didn't ride horses more than they did. Almost every farm had at least one. In any event, they kept work horses, not riding horses. Also, farmers used mules in addition to horses, and only the most adventurous would ride a mule. Due to lack of money, cars and trucks came late to the coves and ridges of Briartown, Happy Top and Camp Branch. I believe the terrain was the major factor. Almost anywhere one went; there was a short cut across the hills and ridges. These were trails, usually too narrow and steep for a horse. Also, it was a cultural thing. People walked, and that was the long and short of it.

When my dad was a kid, any farmer who had a team of oxen or mules was a pretty popular fellow. In addition to bragging rights, he could sell or barter his services; or more often than not, he would just help his neighbor at no charge. Now, most of the Nantahala citizens were of Welsh, Irish, English or Scottish descent which meant they didn't like to be beholden to anyone. The proper thing to do then was to repay with produce, money if they had it, or more often than not, similar services at a later date. In other words, Grandpa Owenby might walk his ox team over to Camp Branch to help Grandpa Mason pull stumps. This service was given from the heart. Three months later, Grandpa Mason might show up at Briartown to help Grandpa Owenby with his harvest. Neither had asked for or expected any payment, but each felt obligated to repay at the first opportunity. When a man got sick or became disabled, it wasn't unusual for neighbors to plow his field for planting or harvest his crops. Again, people didn't expect payment; it was just their Christian duty. And as I have said before, they were the richest poor people I've ever known.

There are several verses in the Bible that tell us to treat our animals well. In Exodus, we are commanded to let our oxen and donkeys rest on the seventh day. In Deuteronomy, we are told not to ignore our neighbor's animals if we find them fallen down by the way. Proverbs 12:10 tells us "a righteous man regardeth the life of his beast, but the tender mercies of the wicked are cruel." In any event, draft animals were far too valuable to abuse aside from whacking with a stick to make them work. Mules were notorious for balking at pulling a plow or hauling a load of produce from the field. They probably received more "whippings" than any other animal. Even so, once back in the barn, they were fed and watered just like the cows. Physical abuse was rare but not unknown.

The Reverend James Wilson, Pastor of Highlands Assembly of God Church, told me a story about a mule back in his good old days. He said the mule laid down in the middle of plowing a field and wouldn't get up. The farmer piled brush next to the mule and set it on fire. When the fire got hot enough, the mule jumped up and ran off across the field. The mule eventually came back home to the barn.

Young men would sometimes race their mules just for the fun of it. Mules were known for their independence and unpredictability. What started out as a race might end up as a mule hunt instead. A mule might throw his rider and take off for the nearest place he could find something to eat.

Dad told me that he and Uncle Troy once got a good whipping for racing two mules from his Great-Uncle Lee's farm to his Uncle Buddy's barn. Grandpa Lorenzo was very straight-laced, and he didn't put up with any foolishness. Apparently, the mules were too keyed up to work when they got them home, and they balked at plowing. When Grandpa attempted to correct the mules, they broke their harness loose from the double tree and took off across the field. Apparently, he didn't know the whys and wherefores of the situation until Uncle Buddy told him the cause. That's when he lit into his two boys, and his method of punishment was not to take away some privilege. It was referred to in politer circles as "tanning hide."

When I was growing up, I heard Dad refer to hinnies, but I thought they were the same thing as a mule. They are not, although many people considered them the same. A hinny is the offspring of a male horse and a female donkey. A mule is the offspring of a male donkey and a female horse. In general, both mules and hinnies are sterile and cannot reproduce because they have a different number of chromosomes. It is now known that a very small number of mules can reproduce, but it is rare. Mules tend to look more like donkeys, and hinnies tend to look more like horses, but sometimes it is difficult to tell them apart. Also, both come in all shapes and sizes depending on the type of horse or donkey used for breeding.

Today, raising mules is more of a hobby than a necessity. In Grandpa's time, they were often the family's means of putting food on the table.

Some farmers preferred mules while others preferred horses or oxen. Again, there are advantages and disadvantages of each. My dad preferred a horse, but I don't know why. Mules live longer and are generally healthier than either horses or oxen but are more difficult to manage. When oxen get too old to plow, they can be used for beef as long as they are reasonably healthy. Horses are easier to manage and if riding is desired, they are certainly the animal of choice. In many cases, the choice of animal was simply economic. One or the other was easily available to a particular farmer while the others were not.

My Uncle Golia Passmore had a mare named Maude he used to lay by his corn. His daughters, three of my first cousins, used to ride Maude. One day, the two youngest, Patsy and Wanda, were both riding at the same time while the oldest, Geneva, led the horse. Something spooked Maude and she took off running across the field with Geneva running along behind hollering "Whoa, whoa!" The girls didn't get thrown off, but it shook them up pretty good. Needless to say, they never rode the mare again.

I can remember riding on the back of a horse down through Camp Branch while Dad led it and Mom walked along side. She was scared of horses and always kept a respectable distance from them. At one time or another, my cousins and I tried to ride anything that had four legs, but our parents made it clear they were work or food animals and were to be treated accordingly.

Gee and Haw

Reverend Oscar Passmore, pastor of Union Hill Baptist Church in Nantahala for several years, had a team of mules named Kate and Dan. They were excellent for plowing fields before planting because of the stronger pull needed for the first plowing or for other uses such as pulling up stumps. Being a kind-hearted man, he would sometimes lend them to his neighbors. Uncle Golie Passmore would borrow them to plow his cornfields. As return payment, he would keep and feed them for a while, thus helping Oscar with his expenses of maintaining the team.

Now, everyone who grew up on a farm is familiar with the terms "gee" and "haw." I always thought they were selected because they were short and sounded different; therefore, they were easier for animals to understand. As it turns out, in Old English, "heyte" meant left and was later transformed into haw. Gee has a similar history. "Ree" meant go and was later modified to gee meaning to turn right. Mules, farm horses and oxen were taught to understand those words at an early age. I can remember playing with my cousins and using those terms instead of left and right. Recently, I asked my cousin, Rachel, if she knew the difference between gee and haw. She replied, "Of course I do, doesn't everyone." Well, actually, everybody doesn't, not any more.

Nita's daddy had a bull named Mose. She said he was the laziest bull on earth. Even though he did his job of bringing in new heifers and bullocks, he wasn't good for much else. He only had one gear and that was super-slow. Furman, her dad, would get on his back and ride in order to get him to go to the barn. Mose would eat grass along the way despite Furman's prodding. He was too big for kids to ride, so one might say he was a one-man bull. In any event, the kids were told to stay away from bulls at all times.

Furman had one of those hay rakes that was very wide, and he had an old mare named Bell. They had her in the back field working. When it came time for lunch, he and the kids who were helping him went to the house to eat. While they were gone, Bell decided she didn't like being alone. She pulled the rake up the little narrow road through the fields, took it through the narrow barn entry and down to the water hole at the branch below the garage. They never did figure out how she got that rake all the way to the house without damaging it.

Back in the good old days, every farm in Macon County had chickens, and a few people raised them to sell. Nita's family on Rose Creek raised them in brooders and sold them by the hundreds. Ditto with eggs. Both my grandmother and my mother talked about bartering eggs for salt, flour or other staples. Laying and settin' hens were well fed and usually kept in a chicken house or coop at night to keep the foxes and raccoons from eating them. Otherwise, chickens roamed freely, pecking in the fields and woods for their food. Chicken was most often eaten for Sunday dinner. My cousins and I would run them down and wring their necks, dip them in a tub of boiling water, pick off the feathers and then give them to our moms for dressing and cutting.

At one time or another, most farms had a mean rooster that delighted in chasing women, kids or anything else that crossed his path. A dog that would tackle a bear would run in fear from a banty rooster on the attack. Clint Grant had such a rooster for a while. We had to go by his house to get to Union Hill Cemetery. That rooster would take out after us coming and going. One day, the rooster disappeared, and I suspect he ended up being Sunday dinner. Later on, our landlady, Annie Powell, had a big dominicker rooster that had spurs sharper than a razor. The old lady told Dad on me for throwing rocks at the old bird. If I could have gotten my hands on it, I would have wrung its neck and taken the whipping.

Ducks were not as common as chickens but people often had them, especially those with ponds or a creek close by. When we lived in the little house above Grandma Emma, we had several ducks. I would chase them to make them quack, and Mom would get after me with a broom. She often served duck eggs for breakfast. I can still remember the taste although I haven't eaten one in sixty years. They were both bigger and richer than hen eggs. When my Aunt Frances was growing up, they had a hard time finding enough to eat. She told me, given a choice, she would always take a duck egg over a chicken egg because there was more food in it.

My great-great Uncle Lee had both ducks and geese. His wife, Lucinda (Lou), would pick the feathers off the geese and make goose down pillows which she sold to neighbors and passers-by. Anybody who had one of her pillows was considered high-falutin. Lee had an oversized wagon he pulled with a team of large horses. Dad said they had big hairy feet so they may have been Clydesdales. He hauled freight back and forth to and from the train depot on the Nantahala River. He used four horses if he had an extra heavy load. Oxen probably would have sufficed, but it would have taken them twice as long to get there and back.

Lee had to have a good brake on his wagon because the winding stairs road was as crooked as a dog's hind leg and steep as a horse's face. That's one road that the State has never improved beyond an annual scraping since it was built back before the Civil War.

Of course, everyone who was raised on a farm has a story or two about oxen, mules and horses. Until motorized equipment came into use, they were the mainstay on farms throughout the Appalachians. In the evolution of farming, they were the link between planting with a stick and modern farm equipment.

It grieves me to know that in today's corporate

farming society, millions of animals are mistreated. Hunger, deprivation, cramped quarters and lifetime discomfort are among the evils heaped upon cattle, hogs, turkeys and chickens. Back in the good old days, edible animals were killed quickly and as painlessly as possible. Draft animals were rarely killed when they became too old to work. They were pastured and allowed to live out the remainder of their lives. After all, if it hadn't been for these beasts of burden, farmers would have had a tough row to hoe, and a large portion of the society at large would have starved.

Edible Meats

Back in the good old days, almost everybody in Burningtown and Nantahala who had a piece of land had swine. Slopping the hogs was usually considered a job for the teenage kids. They were fed twice daily, morning and night. In the summertime, they were fed plantain to supplement their diets. I pulled a lot of plantain to feed Dad's, Uncle John's or sometimes my other uncle's hogs. When I was about five years old, we had a huge red hog roaming freely around the yard and woods. I hated that hog with a passion, and I was glad to eat his bacon, sausage and ham.

Hogs were usually killed in late fall when it was cold enough to keep the meat from spoiling until it could be cured. The men would shoot the hog or hit it on the head with a go-devil. They would cut three saplings and tie them into a tripod. If they had it, they would use a pulley and rope. Dad and Uncle John would tie the rope to a leg and pull it up with a horse or mule. They would cut its throat and let the blood drain out. They would heat a big barrel of water until it reached boiling point. Then they would pour the scalding water on the hog and scrape it. Nita's family would dip the whole hog in a big drum of hot water. Of course, the hog had to be carefully gutted. Once this was finished, the meat was cut up. A clean saw was used for severing the bones. Separating the cuts of meat was not a job for beginners; it required considerably skill to do it right. As the meat was removed from the carcass, it was salted and prepared for storage.

In a way, hogs are amazing animals. They can eat almost anything. In Smoky Mountain pioneer days, they were turned loose to roam the forests where they ate acorns, chestnuts and beechnuts. They consumed roots, worms and mushrooms they dug out of the soil. They could and would eat any fruit that fell from vine or tree. In fact, they would eat anything digestible. A farm family would toss all their leftover food in a bucket and add water or soured milk. This mixture was called "slop" and gave birth to the term "slopping the hogs." Another big advantage for raising hogs is their ability to reproduce rapidly. Sows have a gestation period of only four months, and they grow faster than cattle or sheep. Litters are often a dozen or more. Because of these factors, they were ideal food animals for farmers and pioneers to raise.

Mom and Dad never had beef cattle that I remember. We had a milk cow that liked to kick over the pail, the stool or anything else she could kick. I didn't milk her much since I was too young. Of course, Mom would pour fresh milk in her churn, set it by the stove and let it clabber. Then she would "churn it" until the butter rose to the top. She would skim it off with her hand, wash it in cold water and mold it. My, oh my, how good it tasted with sorghum molasses and a pile of cathead biscuits.

Later, we moved away, and we never owned a cow after that, although I heard Mom say a thousand times, "I sure wish we had a good milk cow." She just didn't like citified milk or butter either. In her senior years, I would hunt around for goat's milk. She said it was good for indigestion which she had frequently. She also liked the taste.

Uncle John kept a couple of beef cows over on "the creek" as he and Grandma called his property up the road just above Happy Top Church. He would slaughter his beef over there and then bring it back to Camp Branch. Grandma would cook stew beef that was mouth-watering good. This was a rarity for me, and I usually ate enough for two adults. They salted down the rest of it, and stored it in the smokehouse. A nice cut of beef in the middle of January sure tasted good.

For reasons I'm not sure of, neither Grandma nor Mom cooked venison. There was plenty of deer around. My cousin Rachel said Uncle Truman was too tenderhearted to shoot deer. I think Dad didn't shoot them because Mom didn't like the smell or taste of the meat. We did have wild turkey once in a while. I can remember biting into a shotgun pellet a time or two. Dad hunted squirrel and rabbit on a regular basis. He didn't like dogs around the house so we didn't have a hunting dog. We just slogged through the fields and woods until we found one. Dad had a sharp eye for seeing them, and most of the time he would have it shot before I saw it. When times were lean, and there were many of them, we had squirrel gravy and corn-bread for breakfast and rabbit stew for lunch or dinner. In the summertime when the garden came in, we had plenty of vegetables to supplement our diet. It was winter when times were hardest.

So it was that animals, both domestic and wild, were an important part of survival in the good old days. Edwin Winslow, in his diary about the first Thanksgiving, wrote about feasting on deer and wild foul. Hernando De Soto brought thirteen pigs with him to the Florida mainland. On his second voyage, Columbus brought pigs with him.

The first cow in America arrived in Jamestown in 1611. Without milk from cows, many more babies would have died in pioneer days. Like their predecessors in Europe, cattle, both male and female, were quickly adapted for plowing and clearing land.

Cortez and other Spaniards brought horses to the Americas in the early 1500's. The Plains Indians quickly adopted them and became expert horsemen. It followed that farmers turned them into draft animals, and later, they bred them with donkeys to produce mules. This hardy animal made major contributions to farming and transportation in the United States.

Over the centuries, animals have truly been man's best friend. God gave us dominion over them, but he also said not to mistreat them. Too many people ignore the second part. I think animals should be treated humanely, regardless of the type or breed. If it hadn't been for animals, the human race would not have advanced as far as it has even though some of that advancement has not been for the best.

I wouldn't want to go back to Grandpa's time, but it certainly had its good points. Many a farmer started out with nothing but a mule and a Bible. Unfortunately, when our society got rid of the mule, the Bible went with it. And that's the downside.

CHAPTER FIVE
Ghosts, Haints and Flying Saucers

Aunt Sarah's Ghost

Granny Hampton was the oldest woman in Clover Lick. No one knew how old she was but the best guess was 102. I had some time on my hands so I ambled over to the dilapidated porch outside Hampton's General Store. I introduced myself and then sat down at the top of the steps and leaned back against a porch post. It squeaked its displeasure at my weight, but it held. She stopped rocking and stared at me for a moment.

"Plasure to meet ya," she said. "What kin I do fer ya?"

I wanted to ask her how old she was but apparently, she read my mind. She gave me a big toothless grin.

"I don't know for sure how old I am if'n that's what ye want to know. The first thing I remember is when my daddy returned home from the Spanish-American War. I was about knee high to a duck. He grabbed me and throwed me up in the air. I thought

I would faint but he caught me and gave me a big hug." She leaned over and spit in an old Karo Syrup bucket.

"Have you been dipping snuff for long?" I asked.

"Longer'n you've bin around," she replied.

"Well, I'm pushing seventy," I said.

She made a noise that was a laugh through a lipful of snuff. "Shoot, sonny, you ain't nothing but a pup. I was dipping snuff when your daddy was still chasing gals. Peers he caught one since yer here."

"He caught one of the best," I replied.

Her aging eyes twinkled. "I kin tell ya liked yer mamma and daddy. My mamma died while daddy was in the war. Hit broke my heart and then daddy's too, when he found out." She stopped talking for a minute and stared off into space. In a moment, she was back. "What ye got on yer mind, son?" she asked. "Ye jist passin' through?"

I changed positions to ease the discomfort in my back. "Guy down the road told me you know some good stories," I told her.

"Oh, he did, did he? That musta bin old Buck. He sends every tourister that passes through here to see me."

"I'm not a tourist," I said. "I just travel around because I love the mountains."

She reached for her bucket and emptied her lip into it. "I reckon I can do without my Rosebud for a few minutes," she said, leaned back in her chair, closed her eyes for a moment and then started talking.

"Back when I was a young girl, my Aunt Sarah died in her sleep. She had lived a hard life, but she'd bin a tough'en. She raised ten girls by two husbands. Both husbands died young, killed in the coal mine just across the hill over yonder. She didn't have no boys. She supported them gals by taking in washin'. She could chop a pile of farwood as well as any man. She had an old bull that she got from old man Simms. He gave it to her in hopes she would marry him but she never did. That bull was a good'n though. People would bring their cow to her and she would charge fifty cents, but if'n the cow didn't calve, she'd give the money back. That only happened twict." Granny leaned forward and laughed. "Anyways, by the time she died, half the people in Clover Lick was her grand-child or great-grandchild.

"Marvin Stauton made a casket out of wormy chestnut. They said it was the purtiest casket ever made in Clover Lick. Her grandsons carried her down the road thar to the Holiness Church. Her family sat up all night with her body. Thar was so many of them that they had to take turns. Jist fore daylight, Sarah sat up in her casket. Liken to scared them that wuz in the room half to death. They all ran outside. Those who wuz outside didn't believe it so they went in. By that time, Sarah had laid back down. They ended up in a big argument about it. Some of 'em thought she was still alive so they waited two days before they buried her. There's still confusion to this day as to what really happened.

"The family got Abe Cartwright to dig a grave fer her. The ground over thar at the cemetery is streaked with coal so it was tough goin' for Abe. Night came and he still wasn't finished. He set a lantern by the grave and kept digging. Two of Aunt Sarah's grand-sons decided that they would have a little fun. They put a sheet over their heads and sneaked up to the grave. They scared Abe so bad that he fainted right thar in that hole. When he come to, he ran over to the church where the family was still settin up with Sarah. He swore that he had seen her ghost. The two boys never fessed up for a couple of years so all those silly people believed Abe.

"Now, everybody was in a tizzy. Auntie had set up in her casket and her ghost was walking around. They didn't know where to bury her or not but they finally got up enough nerve to do it. They were still afraid she might still be alive, so they stuck a pipe in the ground so she could breathe just in case she wasn't dead. The family took turns settin by the grave jist in case Auntie woke up. One night, two of the granddaughters swore they heard her moaning. They tried to get Abe to dig up the grave, but he wouldn't have nothing to do with it. He said she was dead 'cause he had seen her ghost. The family decided to leave her be. When the boys finally fessed up a couple years later, Abe took out after'em with a shovel. He ran'em down along the Greenbrar'River until they jumped in where Abe couldn't reach'em.

"The years came and went. On cold windy nights, people would swear they could hear Auntie moan through the pipe. One time, two men drove over from a college in Charleston. They convinced the family to let them dig up Sarah's grave to see where the noise was coming from. When they pulled the casket out, it was empty. Not one bone was in it. They took the pipe out of the ground but nothing was in it either. They put the casket back and covered it up. For years, several people swore they saw Sarah walkin' round on dark nights."

"Did you ever see Sarah?" I asked.

Granny smiled her toothless grin. "If'n I had, I wouldn't tell it," she said. "I don't want folks thinkin' I'm crazy. Thar's too many loony people round here already."

The Flatwoods Monster

L et me say upfront that I would never make fun of anybody from West Virginia. I mean, shoot, everybody has seen a flying saucer at one time or another, right? On September 12, 1952, an event occurred in the community of Flatwoods that is still talked about today. My older cousin, Earl, a longtime resident of the area will vouch for it. Earl will swear on a gallon of his finest moonshine that several residents of that fine community saw a flying saucer with accompanying alien. The flying saucer was described as a red pulsating ball of light that landed in the woods on the farm of one G. Bailey Fisher.

The saucer was first seen by three local boys when it appeared as a bright object across the sky. The boys then went to the home of their aunt, Kathleen May, and reported they had seen a UFO crash land in the hills.

According to Earl, Ms. May went with the boys to the scene of the outer space visitor. Their dog went on ahead, but apparently the alien scared the bejesus out of him and he ran back to the group with his tail between his legs.

Now, Earl will tell you that it takes a lot to scare a coon hound; which by the way, is the West Virginia state dog. But I digress.

Upon arrival at the scene, the group saw a large, pulsating ball of light and smelled a strange odor. They heard a weird noise and one of them shined a flashlight in that direction. They saw a creature that emitted a shrill hissing noise. Suddenly, it glided toward them and just before they had apoplexy, it changed direction and flew toward the pulsating light.

Panicking, the group took off running and never stopped until they reached the home of Ms. May. She immediately called the local sheriff, Robert Carr.

She then called Lee Stewert, co-owner of the Braxton Democrat, the only newspaper in the county. Once alerted, Mr. Stewert decided to interview anyone and everyone who claimed to have seen the mysterious apparition. At the alleged site of the saucer landing, Stewert reported that a burnt metallic odor still prevailed. On a second visit, he reported two elongated tracks which he believed belonged to the saucer when it landed. It was later revealed that the tracks belonged to a 1942 Chevrolet truck driven by a local person who had gone to the scene just before Mr. Stewert's arrival.

Shortly after the event, a couple associated with the Civilian Saucer Investigation (CSI), a group dedicated to investigating UFO sightings independent of the Air Force, interviewed other witnesses in the area who had reported seeing a similar flying saucer.

One woman told CSI that her house had been violently shaken and her radio had stopped working for the better part of an hour. The director of the local Board of Education swore on a stack of Sunday School Quarterlies that he had seen a flying saucer take off at 6:30 a.m. on the morning of the same day the "Flatwoods Monster" had been seen. Earl said that the director was not a known imbiber, although he did cook a little mash for medicinal purposes. Several of the witnesses interviewed reported they suffered from irritation of the nose and swelling of the throat, with some vomiting. They believed this to be from the mist emitted by the alien creature. A doctor who treated several of the witnesses said that the medical problems could have been brought on by hysteria as a result of seeing the monster.

The Flatwoods Monster was eventually reported nationwide, and in a short time, it became one of the most famous. In 2000, forty-eight years after the event, a Joe Nickell of CSI, concluded that the bright light in the sky was most likely a meteor and that the pulsating red light had been an aircraft navigation beacon. He also concluded that the creature reported by the witnesses was most likely an owl. He believed that the image of the alleged monster (owl) was brought on by a heightened anxiety of observing the meteor and the aircraft beacon simultaneously. Sometime later, the Air Force came to the same conclusion.

As additional evidence, it was known that a meteor had been observed crossing two states besides

West Virginia. They also determined that three pulsating red aircraft beacons were visible from the area where the monster was sighted.

Additionally, Mr. Nickell reported that the shape, movement and sounds reported by witnesses were consistent with a startled barn owl perched on a tree limb. The witnesses had reported that the alien was wearing a pleated green skirt. This was probably green foliage beneath the owl's perch. The heightened state of hysteria in the witnesses caused them to conclude that the owl's talons gripping the limb were "small claw-like hands" which extended in front of the monster. Drawings made from descriptions of the witnesses as being facial features of the monster shaped like the ace of spades were consistent with the face of a barn owl.

In all fairness to the good citizens of Flatwoods, their monster was just one of many UFO sightings in the 1950s. There were sightings in almost every state with Texas leading the pack for the number of sightings. This shouldn't surprise anyone, given that the Lone Star State had more bars and saloons than any other state. To this day, the good citizens of Flatwoods refuse to change their story. They take issue with both CSI and the Air Force. They will be quick to tell you that they saw what they saw and they weren't hallucinating.

Every year, in September, they have a festival celebrating the monster. For you readers who might be traveling to West Virginia in the future, Flatwoods has a monster museum that is open to the public. You might even get to see Kathleen May, who is attending the Green Monster Festival as of this writing. I asked Earl if he had ever seen any flying saucers in Flatwoods. He gave me a sheepish grin. "Only if my wife throws them at me when she's mad," he said.

Fact or Phantom

Not long after my discharge from the Navy, some friends and I decided to investigate the Brown Mountain lights. Their popularity was on the rise at the time. Hundreds of people had tried to solve the mystery, including scientists from the Geological Survey.

About that time, a folk song called The Legend of the Brown Mountain Lights performed by Tommy Faile caused a lot of interest in the lights. We decided we might be the first to determine their origin. We talked to people who had seen them so we could get a good idea of what other people thought. We went to several locations to observe them, including Wiseman's View, Blowing Rock, Grandfather Mountain and the overlook on Highway 181. We found that the overlook was the best place to observe without actually going on the mountain. We also determined that the best viewing time was between 10:00 p.m. and 2:00 a.m. after it rained between 6:00 p.m. and 9:00 p.m.

The lights were fickle. Sometimes they were very active, and sometimes they didn't appear at all.

Our next step was to actually go on the mountain. This was treacherous business because there are cliffs in various locations. Chasing a will-of-the wisp through the woods in the dark could result in serious injury or death. After scouting around on the mountain in the daytime, we realized that we would be restricted to the safer areas. We found an observation tower that was probably built by the Geological Survey. The tower was constructed of four tall poles with two platforms, one at medium height and one near the top. After we felt comfortable we knew where we were at all times, we decided to venture out in the nighttime.

Armed with flashlights, lanterns and binoculars, we started our adventure. One of us would stand at the Highway 181 overlook, one or two of us on the tower, and two or three of us at varying intervals on the mountain. This was in the early sixties, so cell phones had not been invented yet. We devised a set of signals with our flashlights that could be seen between the overlook and Brown Mountain. In this manner, we would try to triangulate on the lights as they started up the mountain. The whole thing was a zoo from the beginning. Someone would yell out, "Here comes one," while the rest of us tried to locate it.

One guy in our group, Charlie, watched as one came toward him. He froze, and it passed right over his head. He said he couldn't breathe, and his skin felt like static electricity from a wool rug. Charlie had a jeep and when a light was spotted, we would all jump in and try to get several of us close enough to jump out and run toward it.

I actually saw one that was as close as fifty feet, maybe less. It was spooky to say the least. It seemed to be almost round, maybe ten feet in diameter, and it looked like pale blue fog with a light in it. I started chasing after it, and it faded away before I could get to it. When I got to where it disappeared, there was a faint odor of something I couldn't identify. The next day, the odor wasn't there. If I had been someone who believed in ghosts, I would have been at the front door of the nearest newspaper claiming to have seen one. Naturally, I would have been the laughing stock of the county. I certainly believe there is a scientific explanation, but I don't have a clue what it is, and apparently, neither does anyone else.

We eventually gave up the chase. For one thing, it took up too much of our time when we should have been doing something else, and secondly, we just weren't getting anywhere. We had scratches from running around in the woods, a deep fear of running off a cliff in the middle of the night and lost companions that took us hours to locate. One night Charlie drove off and left me on the mountain. He said he thought I had left with someone else.

I had to walk out, and before long, my flashlight started going dim. To save the batteries, I would walk in the dark and flip the light on briefly to get my bearings. I was going down an old dirt road with forks all along the way. It was sort of spooky too, although there wasn't anything to be afraid of except a few snakes, wild hogs, wild cats and an occasional bear. Sometime after daylight, I ended up on the highway near Steel Creek Park. I hitched a ride with a guy who worked for Drexel Furniture in Morganton. After that all night walk, I decided I had more important things to do.

There are a variety of opinions among scientists and lay people as to the cause of the lights. In 1913, the U.S. Geological Survey concluded they were train headlights from down in the Catawba Valley. In 1916, a flood wiped out the railroad bridges, and it was impossible for the trains to run for a couple months. Meanwhile, the lights kept going up Brown Mountain. I talked to an old man in Jonas Ridge once, and he told me they were the spirits of dead Confederate soldiers trying to find their way home. He had never seen one himself but he knew people who had. Another legend is that of a slave looking for his master, a planter from down east who got lost during a hunt. The slave came looking for him and persisted night after night. He eventually died, but his spirit still hunts on.

Another legend is supposedly the ghost of a woman who perished around 1850. Her husband allegedly killed her, and the entire community set out to find her body. When they started seeing the lights, they decided that the woman's spirit had come back to haunt them all.

The problem with any theory propounded by European settlers is that the lights appear in local Native-American legends back to about the year 1200. According to them, a great battle occurred between the Cherokee and the Catawba Indians near Brown

Mountain. The Cherokee believed the lights were ghosts of Indian maidens who were searching for the spirits of their braves who died in the battle.

Even today, people still sit at the overlook on Highway 181 and try to see the lights. The best time is still between 10:00 p.m. and 2:00 a.m. although they don't seem as active as they used to be. They rise up from down in the valley and glide slowly up the mountain. The strange thing is they stay about the same distance above the ground until they disappear. They rarely drift up toward the sky, and no two of them vanish in the same place although some people claim they do.

Today, there are two groups who claim to have solved the mystery. One group believes that it is static electricity rising out of fissures in the mountain rocks, and the other group is still sticking with the ghost theory. The one I saw could have been some unknown form of static electricity, but I doubt it. It certainly wasn't a ghost because it didn't say "boo."

Personally, I hope no one ever figures it out. After all, who wants an 800 year-old legend ruined by cold scientific data? Too, I'd hate to go down in history as the only member of my family who actually saw a ghost. My Grandma Emma would say, "I told you so."

Ghosts of the Pine Barrens

While traveling through Chatham, New Jersey, I stayed at the Parrot Mill Inn for about the third time. During breakfast, the owner told me a story about the Jersey Devil, a supposed mythical creature that had harassed people in the Jersey Pine Barrens for over 200 years.

After I concluded my business, I decided to make the two-hour drive to the Pine Barrens. Upon arrival, I was famished so I stopped at a little café. The only customer, I smiled at my waitress, who told me her name was Zena. She was an outgoing, genuine dyed-in-the-wool Pine Barrens native, or "Piney" as they were called. The restaurant closed at 2:00 p.m. Zena volunteered to give me a guided tour for five dollars an hour and a ride home. I took her up on it.

Zena Kallikak told me she was born in a haunted house formerly owned by a sea captain. She claimed the birthmark on her cheek was caused by a haint that scared her mother before she was born.

"A haint?" I asked. "You mean like in ghost?"

"Don't you know nuttin," she said, "of course it was a ghost."

"How long before you were born?" I asked.

"About two years," she said.

"I don't get it. Your mama was scared by a ghost fifteen months before you were conceived. How could that cause a birthmark on you?"

"You're the one who don't get it. It took my pore mama two years to get over it."

"Must have been some ghost."

"I reckon," Zena said. "Mama wouldn't talk about it, though. She'd just sit there staring out the window, looking skeered."

"Maybe we could go there and spend the night," I said. "I've always wanted to see a haint."

"Are you nuts?" Zena said. "You wanna be skeered for two years?"

"I'm willing to risk it if you are."

"All right, smarty pants."

Following Zena's directions, I found the house. It looked like it hadn't been lived in for years. I parked in the yard and we got out and looked around. The house was surrounded by thick bushes on three sides.

"Who owns it?" I asked.

"Some sort of historical group," Zena replied. "They bought it from my daddy after three renters got skeered and moved out."

"Did they see the ghost?" I asked.

"I reckon," she said. "The last renter ran all the way to the police station and babbled something about some big galoot in chains trying to kill him."

"So what did the police do?"

"Nuttin," she said. "They gave him one of them breath tests but he hadn't been drinking."

"Shall we go in?" I asked.

"I ain't skeered if you ain't," Zena replied.

I tried the door but it was locked. I started looking for a window to climb in. I found one on the third try. I crawled through and then opened the front door for Zena. I found my flashlight and wandered around in the house. All I saw was a lot of dust, spider webs and rat droppings.

"This place needs a cat," I said.

"We had one. The haint skeered it off."

"Must be a cat hating haint" I said.

"That haint hates everybody and everything,"

"Wonder why."

"They hung the sea captain for murdering his wife," Zena said. "He claimed he didn't do it, so he hangs around in this old house just waiting to kill somebody to get even."

"Want to spend the night?"

"Where we gonna sleep?"

"I've got two sleeping bags in the trunk of my car."

"Okay, dokey."

We went out and brought in the bags.

"Just remember, this was yore idea," she said.

I decided on the living room and spread my sleeping tarp in front of the old fireplace, laying the sleeping bags on it. "Want to go somewhere and grab a bite to eat?"

"Shore," Zena said. "I could eat a dead possum."

About a mile down the road, I found a diner called the Blue Moon Café. We went in and found a table. The waitress looked like she had gone without sleep for three days.

"We're getting ready to close," she said. "We ain't got nothing left but weenies and beans."

"We'll take it," I said.

The food came with two slices of stale bread and the coffee was old enough to vote. Under normal circumstances, I wouldn't have eaten it, but I was starved. We finished and I went to the register to pay. Zena disappeared into the kitchen and came out carrying a bag. We made our way out to the car.

"What's in the bag?"

"A quart of 'shine," she said.

"I thought you told me you didn't drink."

"I don't," she said, "but this is for my nerves in case we see the haint."

Back at the house, I decided to risk a small fire so I went out back and carried in a couple armloads of dead limbs. I built a fire and we settled into our sleeping bags. I was just about to nod off when I heard chains rattling. I sat up and listened intently. I heard it again, and then I heard the lid on Zena's jar being screwed off. She took a swig.

The noise stopped. I got up and added wood to the fire. Suddenly, I heard chains being dragged down the stairs. I heard the jar lid again. I got the flashlight and went to the stairs. I shined it around but saw nothing. I went upstairs and looked around. Again, nothing. I went back to the living room and crawled back into my sleeping bag. Everything was quiet for a while and then I heard a terrible moaning sound.

Again, the jar lid being removed. The noise finally stopped and Zena started singing. "Row, row your boat, gently down the stream, merrily, merrily; life's but a dream?"

"You scared, Zena?" I asked.

"Heck no, Honey," she said. "I ain't skeered of nuttin." Her voice was slurred.

Suddenly, I heard wicked laughter and more chains on the stairs. Zena jumped up and ran out the front door. I shone my light by her sleeping bag and saw the jar, about half full. I had an idea. I picked it up, carried it to the stairs, took off the lid and went back to the living room. In about two minutes, I heard a gurgling sound for several seconds, and then I heard the noise of chains going back up the stairs. I listened quietly for a while and heard nothing else. I went back to the stairs. The jar was empty. I heard noises outside. I looked out and saw Zena coming across the yard with two deputies. I opened the door for them.

"This young lady says that a ghost is trying to kill you two," the sergeant said.

"I don't know if it's trying to kill us," I said, "but there's definitely a ghost here."

"What kind of ghost is it?" he asked.

"An Irish ghost," I said. The sergeant insisted that we leave the house immediately. I gathered up the sleeping bags.

"Aren't you going upstairs to investigate?" I asked.

"Are you kidding?" he said. "I'd rather tangle with criminals any day. At least I can see them."

The Ghost of Hacker's Creek

My stomach started gnawing on my belt buckle, so I jumped off I-79, took the wrong turn and ended up at the Jane Lew Restaurant on Hacker's Creek Road. As I enjoyed my delicious biscuits and gravy, I became interested in the conversation among six people at an adjacent table. The discussion seemed to center around a Mattie Pettigrew, a local person of some apparent repute. The three ladies at the table were convinced that Mattie was a witch. My ears perked up and I stopped eating momentarily to eavesdrop. Mattie had told someone she had seen the ghost of one, Jane Lewis, the person for whom both the restaurant and the town were named.

As I paid for my breakfast, I asked the waitress where I might find Mattie. She turned three shades of red and then told me to talk to the owner of the hardware store. Not being entirely trusting of outsiders, he asked me whyt I wanted her. When I told him ghost stories interested me, he laughed.

"I gather that Mattie shoots at shadows occasionally," I said, trying to put it politely.

"Not normally," he said, "but this ghost tale of hers has a lot of people wondering if she has lost a few of her marbles. You must be the tenth person that's inquired about her this week." After he asked a few questions, he agreed to tell me how to find Mattie.

"She lives in an old ramshackle house down by Hacker's Creek."

I got back in the truck and followed his directions. When I knocked, Mattie yelled out, "Come in, come in. The door ain't locked."

I pushed the door open and went in. In place of a ceiling, long pieces of rope were stretched from wall to wall. She had hung a multitude of herbs from the ropes to dry. Some I recognized and some I didn't. She sat by the window grinding herbs in a large mortar with a long pestle. A huge cat lay quietly by her chair.

"You come for herbs?" she asked.

"I might take some yellow root if you have it," I replied, "but that's not why I'm here. I'm interested in Jane Lew's ghost."

She stopped her grinding for a moment. "You're not another newspaper reporter, are you?"

I stooped down to pet the cat. "No I'm not," I assured her. "I'm just a curious rambler. Some folks in town told me you had seen the ghost. I also overheard some people say you're a witch."

She laughed. "It must have been those gossipy busybodies that hang out at the restaurant."

I could tell those three particular women weren't her favorites.

"Apparently, you're the only person on Hacker's creek who has ever seen one."

She glared at me. "I don't believe it," she retorted. "The chicken-hearted cowards just won't admit to it."

"That makes sense," I replied. "The owner of the hardware store told me that people have reported seeing Jane's ghost for 150 years."

She rolled her eyes.

"Do you know how the story goes?" I asked. "I've talked to a half-dozen people now, and every one of them has given me a different version."

She thought for a minute. "I'll tell you," she said, "but you'll probably get a seventh version." She closed her eyes for a few seconds, then began....

"As the story goes, Jane Lewis, the mother of the founder of the community of Jane Lew, which bears her name, died under mysterious circumstances. Unfortunately, no one living could remember all of the specifics about her death. She was discovered sitting against a weeping willow tree on the bank of Hacker's creek. She had been found one foggy morning just after daylight by a man looking for his missing horse. It had stormed all night. Strangely, Jane was some two miles from home and yet, according to the man, she was dry as a pine chip. There was no evidence she had been harmed by anyone or by any animal. She was just dead. It was said she could run down a rooster in her bare feet so it was just assumed she was healthy. There wasn't a doctor in a hundred miles but it wouldn't have mattered much; in 1835 doctors were usually self taught.

"Because no one knew the reason Jane died, rumors spread rapidly. There were numerous conjectures as to the cause of her death, but the prevailing theory was that someone sneaked up and smothered her. Most people these days just accept that as fact."

"Have all the ghost sightings been local?" I asked.

"Oh, yes," she replied. "It's always been somewhere along Hacker's Creek."

"Why do you suppose the ghost hangs around?" I pressed.

"Well, again, the story goes that she's looking for the person who smothered her. And since I know you're going to ask, I'll tell you the rest of the story. A fellow named William Cates claimed she was his girl. When she up and married George Hughes, William got very upset and swore he would get even. Shortly after the birth of her first child, George went hunting and never returned. His brothers went out to search for him and found he had been hacked up with an axe. Jane knew William did it, but nobody could prove it. Later on, William tried to get her to marry him but she refused. William then smothered her to keep any other man from having her. So she walks Hacker's Creek on foggy nights trying to find William so she can kill him. She carries an axe so she can chop him up and get even."

"I gather that's the origin of the name, Hacker's Creek," I said

"I suppose so," she replied. "I never did believe

the story myself, or at least I didn't until I saw her ghost."

"Does she look like the typical ghost?" I asked. "You know, wearing a white sheet and all."

She looked at me like I'd lost it. "Heavens no," she continued. "She looked like a real person. She had on a bonnet, a long dress and high button shoes."

"How do you know she wasn't a real person?" I asked.

"I was down by the creek looking for night crawlers with my flashlight," she continued. "I looked up and saw her standing there with an ax in her hand. I almost jumped out of my skin. I shined the light on her and I could see right through her. That's when I knew it was Jane's ghost."

"Well, I'm not one to call you a liar," I said. "There have been ghost sightings throughout history."

She smiled from ear-to-ear. "You're a nice feller," she said. "How much yellow root did you want?"

"Do you have any already ground up?" I asked.

"Sure do," she replied.

"I'll take a pound," I told her.

Before I left, I had also bought Barberry, chicory, milkwort and shepherd's purse.

"How's the herb business?" I asked as she weighed up my order.

"It's been great since word got around that I saw Jane's ghost."

As I walked up the dirt driveway, I met two women coming down. "Is this where the woman who saw the ghost lives?" the tall redhead asked.

"It is," I replied. "I hope you brought some money with you." As I stashed my purchases in the trunk, it dawned on me. "Mattie's not crazy or a witch either. That clever old woman invented the sighting of Jane's ghost to improve her herb business and it has been a smashing success."

Lost Tribes and Flying Saucers

I met Clovalee at a 7-Eleven on Washington Street in Charleston, West Virginia. She walked into the men's room by mistake. Panicky, I rushed out, thinking I was in the wrong room. I wasn't. She came back out without even noticing.

"Are you aware that you were in the wrong restroom?" I asked.

She blushed. "Sorry about that," she said. "I was thinking about the job interview I just had."

"You're supposed to be preoccupied before the interview, not after," I replied.

She was a tall brunette, neat and attractive. "Can I buy you a cup of coffee?" I asked. She looked at me with a penetrating stare, then responded.

"Sure," she said. "There's a great little place down the street. They have the best latte in Charleston. You can help me celebrate my forty-third birthday."

I followed her to a small coffee shop tucked away

between a shoe store and a dress shop. We talked for a couple of hours. The coffee turned into a dinner and a movie. I offered her the opportunity to pick the movie. She took it.

"I'll drive," she said. An hour later, we ended up at the Jungle Drive-in Theatre in Parkersburg. We sat through a double feature; "Close Encounters of the Third Kind" and "The War of the Worlds." In the middle of the second movie, she said she was hungry. She had the Double Jungle Boy Burger with extra onions. It was 1:00 a.m. when we got back to Charleston.

"You got a place to stay?" she asked, knowing full well that I didn't.

"I'll just drive until I find a motel," I said.

"You can bunk on the couch at the house," she said. "My daughter, Kelli, and I sleep upstairs."

Next morning, she went to the grocery store and left me with her fourteen year-old daughter. I thought that was a little foolish, given she had just met me. I quickly learned the daughter was smart as a whip. She could speak three languages and was working on a fourth, Japanese.

"Have you figured out that's Mom's crazy?" she asked.

"Crazy people are a lot of fun," I said.

"I'm not talking about fun crazy," she said. "I'm talking crazy crazy like in certifiable."

"Really," I said. "She seems pretty normal to me."

"Forewarned is forearmed," the kid said.

After Clovalee returned, she fixed a really good breakfast and then I headed out.

Two weeks later, Clovalee invited me back to Charleston, and upon arrival I invited her out to eat. She said she wanted to go to Leonoro's Spaghetti House. She ordered extra garlic. The food was good but not great. We drifted into conversation and she decided to tell me about her background.

"I'm a quarter Choctaw," she said. "I'm sure you know Indians are the lost tribe of Israel."

"Really," I said. "I didn't know that Native Americans had ever been lost."

"You can be a doubter if you like," she said, "but I have historical facts to prove it."

"Actually, I flew on El Al Airlines from Tel Aviv," I replied. "I was on the plane with 400 of the lost tribe and none of them were Indians. In fact, they all spoke Hebrew."

"So, how do you know they were lost?" she asked.

"The plane landed in Newark," I said. "Nobody goes to Newark on purpose." I thought it was a good joke but she didn't seem to get it.

On my third visit, I took the daughter to karate practice. After watching her for a few minutes, it dawned on me why Clovalee wasn't afraid to leave her alone with me. She dropped a big man on the mat like a discarded banana peel. On the way back, she asked how I was getting along with her mom.

"Just fine," I replied.

"Give it a while," she said. That evening she went to visit a friend and Clovalee prepared dinner for us at home.

"I hope you like leeks," she said.

"Where did you get those?" I asked.

"Out in the woods behind the house," she said.

It didn't take a genius to figure out they were ramps. She cut up about twenty and added them to the meat loaf. She nibbled on a couple while she worked. I knew right then I would never kiss her. She was a good cook though. After dinner, we retired to the deck. I was only half listening to her talk when suddenly she got my full attention.

"Did I tell you that I was abducted by aliens five years ago?" she asked.

"Really," I said, deciding to play along. "Where were you when you got abducted?"

"Out in the back yard," she replied. "I saw these brilliant lights go down in the woods back there. Next thing I knew, two of them were standing in front of me. They told me I had to go with them. When I tried to resist, one of them pointed something at me that looked like a small flashlight. After that, I was completely in their power."

"Wow," I thought, "what I would give for one of those."

"How long did they keep you?" I asked.

"Two weeks," she said, "but I only knew that after they brought me back. They doped me up with something and kept me locked in this room with glass walls. Every so often they would hook funny looking wires to me and run tests. When they were done, they implanted a tiny receiver/transmitter in my brain so they can talk to me when they wish."

She stopped talking and stared off into space.

"So how often do they talk to you?" I asked,

breaking the silence.

"Oh, sometimes once a day and sometimes not for a week or two," she said.

"So the voices you hear are in your head?" I asked.

"Go ahead, make fun of me," she said. "Everybody else does."

Just as she finished her story, Kelli returned from her visit. Clovalee went in to wash the dishes. She declined my offer of help. "You can entertain Kelli," she said.

No sooner were we alone when Kelli asked, "Did Mom tell you about her abduction by a flying saucer?"

"I'm afraid so," I said.

"You haven't heard anything yet," she said. "Wait until she starts telling you about reincarnation."

When Clovalee finished the dishes, we played cards for awhile and then turned in for the night. About 3:00 a.m., something woke me up. I heard this little voice in my head saying, "Get out of West Virginia before it's too late."

I left a note for Kelli in her Japanese dictionary and slipped out the back door. At sunrise I was eating French toast and hash browns at Barneys in Mount Airy.

Chain Rattling and Night Lights

When I was a kid growing up on Nantahala, a lot of the local folk believed in ghosts, goblins and the like. Both of my grandmothers had some good ghost stories, and they liked to tell them on dark, stormy nights, especially Grandma Emma. Ghosts were apparitions of dead people who lurked around old houses. People who had seen one claimed they looked similar to a will-of-the-wisp; that is, sort of like a semi-transparent sheet. Goblins were ugly, mean-tempered critters who wore old ragged clothes. No one actually knew anybody who had been hurt by one, but everyone was sure they could and would if given the opportunity.

Now, there were many people who would not walk through a cemetery at night or for that matter, go near one. I was never clear on which of these critters hung out in graveyards, but it was certain that some of them did. Grandma Emma knew of people

who had heard chains rattle and heard heavy footsteps in local cemeteries. As I remember, she had
never actually heard them herself, but then again, she
had never been in a cemetery at night.

After dark, my cousins and I would go to the
Union Hill Graveyard on a dare. Naturally, all three
of us were apprehensive and nervous about going, but
we would die before we would let the other two know
it. Just because our voices quivered didn't mean we
were scared.

My dad said it was all nonsense. He didn't believe in ghosts or any other form of apparition that
haunted houses or roamed around graveyards at
night. He had walked around the Nantahala communities all his young life, often after dark, and he had
never seen or heard one. He told me he and two of his
brothers once sat in the Briartown Cemetery all night
after they had heard reports of an old lady who had
reputedly been buried alive. He finally confessed that
sometime in the wee hours of the morning, they went
to sleep and woke up with the sun shining in their
faces. Naturally, Mom said a ghost had put them to
sleep.

My great-uncle John Owenby told me that back
when he was young and sparking his later-to-be wife,
he rode a horse home across Camp Branch Gap. It
was a moonlit night and there was a strong wind blowing. Something spooked his horse, and it started running. He looked back to see why. He saw something
white flying through the air, and it was coming toward
him. Sort of panicky himself, he kneed the horse to
run faster, which it did. He looked back again and

saw that the apparition was almost upon him. He threw up his arm to defend himself, and it wrapped around his arm. He got the horse stopped, jumped off and started jerking "the thing" off his arm. It turned out to be a bed sheet blown by the wind.

My Aunt Blanche Calhoun told me when she was a young girl living at home, she and her neighbor, Flossie Grant, were down below the house. This was well after dark. They saw a light about two feet off the ground roughly the size of a night light, and it was much too large to be mistaken for a lightening bug. In any event, the light didn't blink on and off; it was steady. There weren't any night lights in those days and no one had a flashlight; in fact, at that time, she probably had never seen one. She said that the light moved slowly toward the house and seemed to disappear into the wall. She and Flossie checked and found no one was or had been outside the house besides them. Later in the night, her grandmother (my great-grandmother), Sarah Jane Mason died. She was in that house. I know my Aunt to be a truthful woman, and I'm sure the story is true. I've also heard other stories of people seeing lights just before someone died.

Most of the Nantahala Folk were quite religious and read the Bible frequently, and of course, there are scriptures that refer to ghostly beings or spirits. We are told not to seek out people who call up spirits or delve into the occult. King Saul cried to God when he saw the Philistine army, but God did not answer him. He told his attendants to find him a woman who was a medium, so he could go and talk to her.

They did as Saul told them and took him to see the Witch of Endor (King James Version: a woman with a familiar spirit). Saul asked her to call up Samuel. She did as she was told. First, she saw Samuel, and then Saul talked to him. Samuel told Saul that the Philistines would defeat him, which they did.

There are several other passages in the Bible that refer to spirits including Leviticus 19:31, 1 John 4:1, Matthew 14:26 and Luke 24:37. Ghost hunters sometimes justify their pursuits by quoting some of these verses. Some people believe ghosts are spirits and some don't. There are over fifty Versions of the Bible, and some use the word "ghost." The King James Version, which is my choice, does not; it uses "spirit." Webster's Unabridged Dictionary defines a ghost as "the soul of a dead person; a disembodied spirit imagined, usually as a vague, shadowy or fleeting form, as wandering among or haunting living persons." I leave it up to the reader to draw his or her own conclusions.

Ghost stories are not restricted to Nantahala. Ghosts and other apparitions are seen, heard and talked about worldwide. Many books have been written about proving or disproving apparitions of one sort or another. Everybody has a ghost story or two of some kind. When I was in the Boy Scouts, our scoutmaster would gather us around the campfire and tell us ghost stories. He may have thought this would make us sleep better. It certainly encouraged us to stay in our tents.

During my tour in the Navy, I attended electronics school in Millington, Tennessee, which is near Memphis. One of my classmates was a local fellow. He told some of us about an old haunted house on the outskirts of town. Being young military guys looking for adventure, we decided to drive over to the house and investigate, and of course, demonstrate our courage. One of the guys had a 1953 Chevrolet, and seven of us managed to squeeze in for the short drive.

Another of the guys, Thibodeau, absolutely believed in ghosts, and he was also a little skittish in general. He had been raised in a bayou near New Iberia, Louisiana. Down in that neck-of-the-woods, almost everybody believed in ghosts, goblins, haints, ghouls and other various and sundry undead types. Some practiced the occult and read fortunes.

In any event, we didn't know we were being set up. The local guy, Pete, and a friend got there ahead of us. The house looked like the one in Alfred Hitchcock's Psycho. It was a large house, two stories and long abandoned. It wasn't locked. Spider webs were everywhere, old dusty furniture, clothing and other paraphernalia littered the house. We wondered around throughout the structure, laughing, telling jokes and having a good time.

The house had a cathedral living room which was perfect for staging a ghost. The perpetrators had stretched a wire across from one balcony to another about twelve feet above the floor. They made a "ghost" out of a sheet and attached it to another wire so they could pull it across from one side to the other. One of them pulled the "ghost" along while the other one made a whooshing noise and shined a flashlight on it from the second floor.

Thibodeau panicked and ran charging out the door, knocking a couple of the other guys down. There was general pandemonium for a couple minutes until the two jokesters started laughing. By that time, our Cajun friend was a half-mile down the road. After some nervous laughter, name calling and general camaraderie, we all piled back in the car and set out to find our missing buddy. By the time we found him, he was halfway back to the base.

My guess is the old house was eventually torn down to make room for a housing development or a shopping center. I've always wondered where ghosts go when their homes are torn down. Maybe they lurk around in the attics of all those shopping centers. I've also wondered where the chains come from that ghosts and goblins rattle at night. Nobody buries people with chains in their grave. Maybe they sneak into hardware stores at night and steal them. Or maybe logging chains disappear on a regular basis.

Anyway, I'm like my dad, I don't believe in ghosts either. But just in case I'm wrong, I ain't hanging out in any cemeteries at three in the morning. And I ain't gonna ask any medium to call up spirits of the dead either. There are some people I just don't want to see again.

Swamp Fever

I first met Thibodaux in the chow hall at the Navy Electronics School in Memphis. The name itself told me he was Cajun, but at that time, I knew little about his people. In hindsight, he was one of the most interesting people I've ever met. He believed in ghosts, witches, haunted houses and cemeteries and all the other scary stuff that allegedly happens in the swamps and bayous in southern Louisiana.

He had a collection of old Jimmy Noone jazz records that he kept in his locker. He was horrified when I told him that I had never heard of the man. Apparently, Jimmy was to the Cajuns what Elvis was to the rest of the world.

When Thibodaux suggested I go home with him over the Thanksgiving holidays to Cut Off, Louisiana, I decided to take him up on it. It was certainly preferable to hanging out on the base and eating canned turkey. We left early and drove due south through Mississippi, stopping only for a quick meal at the

Crawdad Hole in Jackson. The seven hour drive put us in Cut Off by 4 p.m.

His family's house was on an unpaved street that ran along Bayou Lafourche. Across the road and down the street was an old two-story unpainted house. According to Thibodaux, no one had lived there for at least fifty years, and it was haunted. He believed, and apparently so did everyone else in Cut Off, that anyone who entered the house would come down with swamp fever. When I asked what swamp fever was, he didn't know except to say the person went mad and broke out with a horrible rash.

Upon arrival, we found Alyssa, his mom, preparing a Cajun feast. He had two sisters who were cuter than a pair of speckled pups. After a lot of hugging and kissing, Thibodaux's dad, Boudreaux, explained why his wife was cooking in three iron pots hanging in the huge fireplace. After all, they did have a wood cooking stove.

"First of all," he said, "it's our tradition, but secondly, it tastes so much better than food cooked on the stove."

The main dish was seafood gumbo made with shrimp, catfish, black drum and an assortment of vegetables. The jambalaya had rice, duck and beef well seasoned. She had also prepared a big plate of frog legs which turned out to be my favorite. The long table was filled from one end to the other, but I don't remember all the other dishes. Boudreaux told me they often ate crawfish, alligator, squirrel, rabbit and turtle but they usually didn't when they had guests because outsiders were often finicky. Their language wasn't that different from mine but to demonstrate their dialect, they talked in Creole Cajun for a couple of minutes just to give me a sample. I confess I understood very little.

After a delicious dinner, I got quite a reaction when I asked if I could go over and visit the haunted house. I thought Alyssa was going to choke and Boudreaux launched into a diatribe about why I should stay away from that evil place. Having settled that, Thibodaux invited me to walk around town with him. Driving wasn't needed because everything was within ten minutes walking distance.

We ended up in a run down but very active place called the Hornet's Nest. In hindsight, I think the run down look was just part of the Cajun décor. Upper class would not have been considered respectable. The feature act was a singer by the name of Joe Barry. His music was more or less a Cajun version of Rock and Roll, but I did enjoy hearing him sing.

We got back to the house well after midnight. I was still wound up from dancing with several women.

After about an hour or so, it seemed that everyone was asleep but me. There was some serious snoring going on, so I dressed quietly and slipped out the back door. Once outside, I realized there was a full moon. I ended up in front of the so-called haunted house. After about ten minutes of staring at it, I decided to try the front door.

It wasn't locked; in fact, it almost fell off in my hand. There were several windows with panes missing and one window was completely gone.

The moonlight was good enough for me to see

how to move around inside. I carefully tested the stairs to make sure they would hold me. Just as I reached the top, an owl flew out from somewhere in a bedroom, passing so close that a wing hit me in the face. I lost about a year's growth and decided to go back downstairs. About halfway down, I heard something that sounded like a chain dragging. I stopped and held my breath. As I eased a little farther down, the sound got louder and I knew it was definitely a chain. My dad had logging chains but it didn't sound like one of those. It had a tinnier sound. But then what respectable ghost would be dragging a heavy logging chain.

As I eased farther down, the noise started up again. Clearly, it was being dragged across the floor. The noise dimmed somewhat, giving me the impression it had gone into another room. Despite my bravado, my heart was beating a little harder than normal and I realized my hands were sweaty. Suddenly, the noise came back toward me and then banged against something. I had now reached the bottom of the stairs.

I realized the ghost was getting closer every second. I made a dash for the front door and as I ran outside, it occurred to me that it might grab me from behind. I turned around for a quick look.

The ghost was somebody's dog that had broken loose from wherever he'd been tied, and he was still dragging his chain. When I stopped and turned around, he began wagging his tail. After my heart slowed down, I went back and petted him. Since he was following me back toward the house, I stopped at the car, fished out a pack of cheese crackers and fed him. I unfastened his chain and threw it into the bayou. Satisfied with his snack, he turned and headed back down the street.

I slipped back into the house and went to bed. Next morning, I kept my mouth shut about the ghost, knowing I would probably be evicted from the premises if I blabbed. I told Thibodaux about it on the way home. To say the least, he was flabbergasted. He watched me carefully for several days to see if I were going to come down with swamp fever. He even tried to get me to go to sick bay for a checkup. Of course, I never did get sick.

Thibodeaux said later that the good witches must have been watching out for me.

Sweetwater Sally

According to Dad, he had just turned eighteen when his Uncle John invited him to go to Sweetwater, Tennessee, to work in a lumber camp. Dad was young and eager for adventure and Uncle John (my great-uncle) would try anything twice. Both of them had nerves of steel and both would fight a circle saw when they were mad. Mom often said Dad was just like Uncle John in many ways. She wasn't necessarily paying him a compliment. I think that's probably the reason Uncle took a liking to Dad. Back in the thirties and forties, they spent a lot of time together working on jobs, mostly logging, but also farming and preparing food for the hard Nantahala winters. Both of them were interested in ghost stories. They would tell them; repeat them and sometimes, they would try to debunk them.

They hadn't been in Sweetwater long when they found out ghost stories abounded in that area of Tennessee. In those days, men worked hard, especially in wood camps. At the end of the day, they were usually too tired to pursue personal interests beyond resting or playing cards. Still, they had the weekend to wander around and check out the area, mostly on foot.

As it turned out, Uncle John knew someone in Sweetwater who had a 1925 Model T Ford. Apparently, they spent about as much time keeping it running as they did in riding. He said a man had to be careful when using the hand crank. If one didn't turn it loose soon enough, the engine would kick it back and possibly cause serious injury. Also, the gas tank was under the front seat. Still, it beat walking and they did get to see a little of the area on their weekends off.

Some co-worker in the wood camp told them a story about the ghost of Sweetwater Sally. As soon as the weekend came around, they set out to investigate. The town only had a couple of streets in 1928, so it wasn't hard to ask questions. The first person they asked told them to go see Liza Pitman, a woman reputed to be 102 years old. Liza was easy to find and her granddaughter, who lived with her, invited Dad and Uncle John inside. They found the old woman sitting in the parlor with a shawl draped across her lap. She was sewing quilt pieces. "So you want to hear about Sally's ghost," the old woman said.

"We do," Uncle John replied. "Would you mind telling us the story?"

"There ain't much to tell," Liza said, "but I'll tell ya all I can. The house is over yonder on Price Street. It's faded yeller and hit's two stories. I was living over in Ten Mile when the ghost was first seen, but I've heard it many times. Sally was six years old when she came down with smallpox. Her bedroom was upstairs facing the street. Her mother wouldn't let her out of the room for fear of infecting other people. The little girl would pace the floor and at night, people could see her shadow go back and forth between the window and the lamplight. Finally, she got too sick to get out of the bed. Sally's mother knew the little girl was going to die so she went to get help. While she was gone, Sally died.

"People who claim to have seen the ghost say they hear an ear-splitting scream and then they see a little girl walking in front of the house carrying a pink blanket. There are different stories about what happens after they see her. Some say she just disappears into the wall of the house. Others say she just fades away when they try to approach her. Most people just git plain skeered and run off.

"Mostly, people say they see Sally's shadow passing across the window in front of the lamplight. I've seen that myself, but I've never seen Sally carrying the blanket. If you men are really interested, you can go there. Sid and Mavis Tolly live downstairs in the house. Nobody lives upstairs. Out of respect, Sid lights a lamp in the bedroom every night and lets it burn until the oil runs out."

Uncle John and Dad decided they would investigate. They went in and told Sid and Mavis so they wouldn't scare them. Sid told them to go ahead; they were accustomed to people doing that. They walked back and forth in front of the house to see if they could see Sally carrying the blanket. After two nights of pacing up and down the street, they decided they weren't going to see Sally carrying the pink blanket. They had seen the shadow passing across the window. They figured it was probably Sid doing it to perpetuate the ghost story. They asked him if Dad could sit in the room while Uncle John watched outside. Sid agreed. The next night, Sid lit the lamp and left Dad sitting in a chair against the wall. As Uncle John watched, the shadow passed in front of the window just as it had before. Dad saw nothing on the inside. They switched places. Now, Dad saw the shadow and Uncle John didn't.

Refusing to believe in Sally's ghost, they kept watching and observing. They tried it on windy nights, still nights, clear nights, rainy nights, moonlit nights and completely dark nights. The results were always the same. Finally, they gave up and accepted the shadow crossing the window as a mystery unsolved. Dad said Sally's ghost was like the Brown Mountain lights. There had to be a reasonable explanation, but he didn't have a clue. Price Street still runs through Sweetwater. The two-story yellow house was old when Dad was young. It's probably long gone now. The story about Sally is still alive and well. And who knows, perhaps Sally's ghost is alive and well also. Price Street has a sidewalk so it's easy to walk along at night and watch for a shadow to move across a second story window. Want to try your luck? That is, if you believe in ghosts.

Harley's Ghost

Not long after my discharge from the Navy, I worked part-time at the Ribet Motel in Valdese while attending Lenoir-Rhyne College. At some point, the owner conned me into supervising the waitresses. It didn't take long to figure out they were an unreliable bunch.

One Saturday morning, I hired a twenty year-old from Spruce Pine by the name of Jean Collins. She was reliable, personable and showed up for work on time. I had made a point of not dating anyone who worked for me, but Jean was so cute I made an exception. After about three months, she got homesick for Spruce Pine and moved back in with her mom on Rabbit Hop Road, a few miles out of town. She made a point of telling me, "Now, I'm not leaving you, I'm just leaving Valdese. If you want to date me you'll have to come to Spruce Pine."

When I could get some free time, I would drive

up that steep winding mountain road and on to her mom's house on Rabbit Hop. Even though Jean was almost twenty-one, her mom, Wilma, thought it was her God-given right to supervise Jean's dates. She even went so far as telling Jean, in front of me, that if she did anything unladylike, a ghost would get her.

At first, I thought she was joking, but I soon realized she was dead serious, no pun intended. This resulted in us sneaking off to some side road or other quiet location to get away from Wilma. At age 23, I felt a little silly hiding out from my date's mom. After trying several locations, we found an abandoned house with four old rocking chairs on the front porch.

The first time we went there, a full moon stood low in the sky. Jean commented that rocking in the moonlight was the most romantic thing she had ever done. The second time, she told me the house was supposed to be haunted. I asked her where she had gotten that information since she hadn't mentioned it the first time.

"My mom told me," she replied. I wondered how momma dearest knew we had been at the old house, but I didn't ask. Instead I asked her how it was haunted.

"Well," she said, "the owner, Harley Jones, had been found in bed stabbed to death. People who knew him said he had abused his wife for many years and after she died, she came back to get even."

I told Jean I didn't believe in ghosts at which point she told me she certainly did. After all, Mamma said they existed and that was good enough for her.

It was obvious she was a little nervous since her

mom had put the fear of ghosts in her. I didn't want her to be afraid so I broke into the house, took a flashlight with me and looked around. Finding nothing, I told her to relax and enjoy the evening. All went well for about an hour and then we heard a noise that sounded like someone rocking on the other end of the porch. There was no moon that night, so I couldn't see all that well. I clicked on the flashlight and saw a chair rocking back and forth.

"Oh Dear Lord," Jean said. "It's old man Harley's ghost."

Not wanting my romantic evening ruined, I walked over to the chair and waved my hand back and forth between the arms. I felt nothing that seemed like a ghost, so I grasped the chair arms and stopped the rocking. I watched it for a couple minutes to see if it would start rocking again.

When it didn't, I walked back over to my chair and pushed it closer to Jean. Things went well for a few minutes and then we heard the chair rocking again. I got up, went across the porch and stopped it for the second time.

"This is getting a little bit ridiculous," I said, walking around the porch, shining the light under it, trying to determine what was causing the chair to rock. Unfortunately, I found nothing. When it started rocking a third time, I went over, picked up the chair and set in out in the yard. I kept an eye on it for a while to see if it would rock in its new location. When nothing happened, I ignored it and turned my attention back to Jean.

Soon, we were sitting in our respective chairs

holding hands and whispering sweet nothings.

Suddenly Jean pulled her hand away and said, "What's that noise?"

"I don't hear anything," I said, but I did. When it became obvious the romance was on hold until I investigated the new noise, I turned on my flashlight and shined it around on the porch. The other chair adjacent to the first chair was rocking all by itself. Now, I was beginning to wonder if the house really was haunted.

Thinking it might be the wind; I stuck my finger in my mouth and then held it up to see if any breeze was blowing. There seemed to be no motion at all. This time, I got up, took my flashlight and walked all around the porch, looked thoroughly under the porch and then went into the house. I had decided someone was playing a trick on us. After all, her mother did know we were there. When I found no one, I went back out on the porch.

"Tell you what, Jean," I said, "Let's move all the chairs off the porch and see what happens." Then we sat on the steps for awhile and just watched the porch. When nothing new happened, I told her the crisis was over.

I went to my truck, got a tarp out of the back and unfolded it on the porch. We sat there for a while and talked as I waited patiently to see if anything else would happen. By midnight, nothing unusual had occurred. I leaned over and kissed her on the cheek. When she responded favorably, I kissed her again. We stretched out and started necking.

Suddenly Jean sat up and hollered, "Oh Lord,

stop me before Harley's ghost gets me for doing something unladylike."

After that, we just held hands and talked. About 2:00 a.m., I drove her home. I didn't kiss her goodnight because Wilma was looking out the window.

A few days later, I found out Jean was also dating another guy, apparently two-timing us both. I checked out.

About ten years later, I stopped off at a restaurant in Linville Falls, and to my surprise my waitress was Jean. She looked as good as she did the last time I saw her, if not better.

"Seen any ghosts lately?" I asked.

"There's one upstairs in the attic where I live," she replied.

"Maybe old man Harley's ghost changed locations," I surmised.

"No, his wife's ghost did," she stated.

I looked at her for a moment trying to decide if she was pulling my leg. Apparently, she wasn't. "Why did she move in with you?" I asked.

"You scared Harley off, and she got lonely," Jean replied.

"I hope she's happy living with you," I ventured.

"We keep each other company since Mama died," she replied. She went to the kitchen to turn in my order. I wondered if Mama had a ghost wondering around somewhere. It occurred to me I didn't want to know. I left a ten dollar bill on the table and slipped out the back.

CHAPTER SIX

A Hunting We Will Go

And the Winning Coon Is....!

After a business meeting in Albuquerque, I decided to drive back to North Carolina. I was tired of flying, and I wanted to revisit some of the country I hadn't seen in years. I rented a mid-sized car and headed out. I spent the night with an old Navy buddy in Norman, Oklahoma. We talked until midnight about the good old days. I nursed one beer while he downed about ten.

Next morning, I sympathized with his hangover before heading out. I had promised my fourth cousin on my mamma's side, Grinder Dills, I would stop off in Blue Ball, Arkansas, for a visit. I should mention Grinder got his name because he began grinding his teeth in his sleep while he still had baby teeth. His mom and dad couldn't cure him of it, and of course, he had never seen a dentist in his life.

His family prided themselves on being natural folks, and of course, that included skipping baths regularly.

Grinder started chewing tobacco when he was six by snitching cuts of homegrown twists out of his grandfather's barn loft. The last time I saw him, the color of his teeth matched the color of his rusty old Ford truck.

I arrived in Blue Ball at noon. I figured I would eat before driving over to Grinder's house; that is, if I could find it. It only took me a minute or two to figure out there wasn't a whole lot going on in Blue Ball. An old country store that had been closed for years stood by the dusty road, and next to it was a small diner with a hand painted sign that proudly announced, "Cooter's Burgers."

While I waited on my Cooter Burger and Freebird Fries, registered trademarks, according to the owner, Bocephus Cooter, who told me he got the name, Bocephus, because he was conceived during the Lynrd Skynrd song of the same name. He had been born in Possum Grape but had moved to Blue Ball to open his burger stand. His business philosophy was also hand painted on the wall behind the grill, "If your burger ain't warm, it didn't come from Cooters." He gave me directions to Grinder's house which was about as complicated as a physics exam. On the way out, I bought a black and white Cooter Burger trucker cap for $12.50, twice the cost of the meal.

"Tell you what," Cooter said, "You're a nice feller; I'll get my sister, Selma, to drive ahead of you so you won't get lost; that's her car across the road there."

It was the only car around that wasn't over twenty years old; a red Corvette.

"She must have a good job," I commented.

"Yeah," he said, "she's in sales. She goes over to Ft. Smith on Thursday and comes back Sunday afternoon with a pocket full of folding money."

I decided to take him up on his offer because I had already forgotten half the directions. I fell in behind Selma just as she pulled onto the road. I hung on to my Cooter Burger cap as she negotiated one curve after another, driving just below suicide level. I soon realized I'd never find my way back because I didn't have time to watch anything but Selma's bumper.

Grinder's driveway, if one could call it that, circled around the barn and then by the house. Selma never stopped; she just pointed to the house as she flew by. The only reason I knew I had arrived was because Grinder was standing in the yard, leaning against the rusting hulk of a 1949 Ford. Being a true redneck, he introduced me to his dogs before he did his wife.

We went out back behind the house to the dog lot. A bunch of redbone coonhounds roamed around the enclosure. "I count eight," I said. "What are their names?"

"Well," Grinder began, "that one there in the front is Dasher, the next one is Dancer, and the ones in the middle are Prancer, Vixen and Comet and those in the back are Cupid, Donner and Blitzen."

"That's pretty original," I said. "So, where's Rudolph?"

"Back there in the big doghouse," he said and then whistled. Out came a big ugly dog showing his teeth.

"What in the world is that?" I asked.

"Oh, he's half Doberman and half pit-bull," he answered.

"That ain't no coon dog," I said.

"I guess we'll find out tonight," Grinder replied. "You're going with me, ain't you?"

"I suppose," I said. "It's not my thing, but I've been a time or two."

We went into the house, and he introduced me to his second wife, Cora. She was a cute blonde about half Grinder's age.

"Looks like you've done very well for yourself," I said.

"Yeah," Grinder whispered. "She's cute but she ain't too bright."

Couldn't be if she married you, I thought, but didn't say. We sat down to supper. Cora dished up fried potatoes, cornbread and what looked like chicken pot pie. I loaded up my plate with the potatoes.

"What's the meat dish?" I asked politely.

"It's possum pie," Grinder said proudly. "That Cora is a good cook" he bragged as he passed the bowl to me. I passed it on to Cora.

"You ain't eating the pie?" she asked.

Thinking quickly, I replied, "I'm a vegetarian."

"What's that?" Cora asked.

"That's a guy who can't shoot straight," Grinder said and laughed at his own joke.

A few minutes after dark, Grinder and I walked out on the porch. A full moon stood in the sky.

"Good night for coon hunting," Grinder said. He loaded the dogs in the back of his truck and we headed out. The dogs were excited and barked and bayed all the way. We stopped at the end of an old forest service road and Grinder let the dogs out. "Go get him, boys," he said.

The dogs disappeared in a hurry. We followed, listening to the sounds of the baying. He kept Rudolph on a chain and let the dog run slightly in front of him. After an hours or so, Grinder stopped climbing. "Listen to their baying," he said. "My boys have treed a coon."

I listened but they didn't sound any different to me.

We finally reached the tree with Rudolph pulling hard on his chain. Grinder shined his light up into the limbs. "There he is," he said. "He's a big 'un. Here, you hold Rudolph. I'm going to rock him out of the tree."

He quickly gathered several rocks and stacked them in a pile. "All right, Roy, you shine the light while I throw up at him." About the tenth throw, Grinder hit the coon, and he fell out of the tree.

Just as he hit the ground, Rudolph jerked the chain out of my hand and headed for the coon. I figured he would kill the critter with one bite, but I was wrong. As the coon went down on his back, he swiped Rudolph across the face with his sharp claws. I saw blood spurt out of the dog's nose. Rudolph gave a loud howl and took off down the hill. All eight hounds took off after him.

"Geeze," Grinder said, "I'm embarrassed; Rudolph is a wimp."

"You'd be a lot more embarrassed," I added, "if

you had named him Killer."

The coon stood on his hind legs, waving his front paws in the air like a prize fighter who had just gone nine rounds and won. Grinder flew mad, grabbed his .38 out of his holster and shot at the coon. The critter stood there defiantly, and Grinder missed him three times. The coon finally turned and ran into the underbrush with Grinder firing at his backside. He emptied the gun and missed every time.

"Well Grinder," I said, "it looks like I'm not the only vegetarian in the family."

Kentucky Justice

I left home at 3:00 a.m. headed for Pioneer Village in London, Ontario. I'd been on the road for about four hours and I was getting hungry. I decided to drop off I-75 onto Stinking Creek Road and swing over toward Flat Lick, Kentucky. There was a great little diner near there and I had connections; namely, the cook.

My first visit to Flat Lick had been curiosity about the community's name. Around a sharp curve and down a steep hill, I had seen a sign that read, "Os-sums Roa sid Din." *(I learned later the sign originally read, "Possums Roadside Diner.")* I didn't realize it was a Café until I was almost even with it. Putting my foot down hard, the car slid across the gravel parking lot for about twenty feet. I had to walk past several pickup trucks to get to the door. The trucks averaged about five dogs each in cages on the back. The dogs

raised such a ruckus when I passed, I thought someone would come outside and check, but they didn't.

Once inside, I saw the health inspection certificate displayed prominently on the wall behind the
counter. There was a big bold "B" on it. The waitress
and co-owner, Roxie Lee, saw me staring at the sign.

"It's because of the floors," she said. "These redneck customers keep spitting tobacco juice on it. I'd
run'em off, but I need their business. I'll tell you what,
honey; I can see you're concerned about cleanliness,
so you come with me."

I followed her into the kitchen. An elderly
woman was doing the cooking, and the kitchen was
spotless. "This is my mamma," Roxie Lee said. "Her
name is Bonnie Jo."

"Pleased to meetcha," Bonnie Jo said. "Welcome
to Possums." She weighed about 95 pounds soaking
wet. Roxie Lee, on the other hand, would have pegged
the scales at about 220.

"Like mother, like daughter sure doesn't apply
here," I thought.

"If'n you warsh your hands good, you can sit in
the kitchen with me," Bonnie Jo said. I went over to
the sink and washed them thoroughly. I didn't want
to be evicted by a woman half my size. "You can sit at
the table there," Bonnie Jo said. "I'll fix you whatever
you want and you can pay Roxie Lee on your way out."

"You got any good biscuits and gravy?" I asked.

"You gotta be kiddin' me, honey," she said. "I
make the best biscuits and gravy in the state of Kentucky."

"In that case, I'll have a double order," I said. In

a couple minutes, she plunked a large platter down in front of me. There must have been a half-pound of crispy bacon on the side. I didn't order the bacon but I had no intention of upsetting Bonnie Jo.

"We have pork brains if you'd druther have them," she said. I could tell she was waiting for my reaction.

"No thanks," I said. "My daddy liked them, but I could never bring myself to eat them."

Bonnie Jo laughed. "I hate'em too, but these local boys love'em."

By the time I had finished eating, I was in full agreement with Bonnie Jo. Her cooking was outstanding.

"Where you from, honey?" she asked.

"Franklin, North Carolina."

"Where's that?"

"It's near Cherokee."

"I know where that is," she said and grinned from ear-to-ear. "Possum and me spent our honeymoon there."

"I gather your husband's nickname is Possum."

"Late husband," she said.

"I'm sorry. "How did he die?"

"He fell out of a tree on his 65th birthday."

"What in the world was he doing up in a tree at that age?" I asked.

"The old coot was coon huntin'," she said.

Sort of at a loss for words, I asked her how he acquired his nickname.

"When he was young, he used to sell possum hides to the Ebenezer General Store for a nickel apiece. He brought in so many hides old man Ebenezer started calling him possum. The name stuck."

"You have other children besides Roxie Lee?" I asked.

"She's an only child," Bonnie Jo said. "We raised her right, though. She doesn't smoke, drink or cuss, and she goes to church every time the door opens."

Now, I was arriving for about my tenth visit, and I'd looked forward to Bonnie Jo's biscuits and gravy for several hours. I had to walk past the usual row of pickup trucks and listen to the dogs bark.

When I walked through the door, Roxie Lee came over and gave me a bear hug. She could move fast for a big woman. Despite her weight, I always marveled at how pretty she looked. "Don't sit down until you go see Mom," she said. "She'll skin us both if she doesn't get to talk to you."

Trying to get my breath back as I walked, I headed for the kitchen. Bonnie Jo stood in front of the grill. "Well, if you ain't a sight for sore eyes," she said. She pointed to the table where I usually sat. It was covered with livermush, pork brains and pieces of chicken. "Sorry, you're table is covered up," she said. "If I'd a knowed you was comin', I'd a had it ready for ya."

"I've got an idea," I said. "Why don't you come out and sit with me; I'll buy your breakfast."

"Honey, there ain't no man bought my breakfast since possum died," she said. "All right, I'll do it. These rednecks can wait a few minutes." She hollered out the kitchen door; "Roxie Lee, take over for me while I have breakfast with my friend."

Bonnie Jo picked out a table in the back corner. We talked while we ate. Roxie Lee came over and sat with us for a couple minutes until some scruffy looking customer bellowed for more coffee.

As I looked at her retreating back, I asked Bonnie Jo if Roxie Lee had ever been married. "Sure was," she said, "but she's a widow like me." I didn't ask for more information, but Bonnie Jo continued. "Her husband beat her a lot. When Possum found out about it, he got so upset, he cried. The next day, he invited Donald Ray...that was her husband's name...to go deer huntin' with him. Donald Ray never came back.

" After a couple days, Possum went to the sheriff's office and reported him missin'. He told them Donald Ray and him had split up like deer hunters do. The sheriff sent out a search party and on the third day, they found him layin' face down in a creek with a broken neck. There was a cliff right above his body. It had rained hard the night before, and they weren't able to tell for shore if he had fallen off the cliff. They asked Possum a lot of questions, but he kept tellin'em he never seen Donald Ray after he went off on his own. They had some kind of inquiry and declared it a huntin' accident."

"I suppose one could call that Kentucky justice," I said. Bonnie Jo's eyes sparkled when she looked at me.

"I've never heard it called that," she said, "but you hit the nail on the head."

"You think Possum killed him?" I asked and

then apologized immediately. "I'm sorry, Bonnie Jo; I shouldn't have asked that."

"That's all right, honey," she said. "I've always believed he did, but he never said, and I never asked. Some things are best left alone."

I finished my breakfast, gave Bonnie Jo a hug and hit the road. I thought about Possum and his son-in-law as I drove along. My daddy despised wife beaters. I once asked him why, and he said the Bible tells us to show the same love for our wives as Christ did for the Church. Donald Ray obviously never read that verse. I settled back in my seat for the long drive.

"Nobody will ever know what really happened to Donald Ray except maybe Possum," I thought. "And dead men tell no tales."

Games with the Game Warden

I had certainly picked a beautiful morning to start my camping trip in Monongahela National Forest in West Virginia. As a lifelong tree hugger, I thoroughly enjoyed the vast deciduous forests unfolding before me. I found a good spot where I could back my truck up to the edge of a large creek and pitched my tent before the sun reached its zenith. I decided to try my luck at fishing even though I didn't have a license.

In a couple hours, I caught enough for a good supper. I cleaned my fish on the bank and threw the chum in the creek because I didn't want anything lying around that would attract bears. I built a good fire and let it burn down to hot coals. I got my oil, cornmeal and pan out of the back of the truck and began frying the fish. Just as I got caught up in the aroma, I heard a vehicle coming down the road.

As it rounded the curve just about my camp, I

saw the sign on the side that read, "West Virginia Division of Natural Resources." Uh oh, I thought. The officer got out of his truck and walked over to my camp.

"Frying up some fish are you?" he smirked.

"Sure am," I said. "Care to eat with me?" He stared at me for a moment. "Do you have a fishing license?" he asked.

I knew I needed to answer in a very polite manner. "I don't think I need one," I replied.

"You do if you caught them here in the creek," he replied. Then he gave me his "I gotcha look."

I tried not to look nervous. "Nah," I said, "I bought them from a guy over in Staunton, Virginia, who was selling them out of the back of his truck."

He gave me that, "I don't believe you for a minute" look. He began walking around my campsite, making bigger and bigger circles. I knew he was looking for fish parts.

I breathed a silent "Thank You, Lord," because I had thrown all the parts in the creek. My fishing rod was in the back under a tarp. I figured if he searched the truck, he had me. He didn't. Satisfied he wasn't going to find anything, he came back over to where I was cooking.

"Looks like you got away with it this time," he stated, "but don't push your luck." I wasn't sure how to answer.

"Sure you don't want to stay for supper," I replied. "There's enough for both of us."

Apparently, this guy liked to intimidate people by staring at them. I stared back.

Finally, he spoke. "It's tempting," he said, "but I might be party to a crime." He laughed for the first time. "Have a good dinner," he said and walked back to his truck.

I finished my meal and washed the dishes. As darkness began to fall, I wondered how many bears roamed around that part of the forest. There isn't any close by, I concluded, or they would've smelled my fish and come in for a visit. Stowing the dishes away, I got the webbed chair out of the back and found a good place to sit. A few clouds scudded across the sky and the full moon shone in all its glory. I sat quietly for a long time.

A family of raccoons came out of the woods and started fishing. I could hear them crunching on crawdads. I must have watched them for close to an hour. Finally, their hunger satisfied, they slipped back into the woods. Knowing there were lots of bears in the Monongahela, I decided to sleep in the back of my truck rather than in my tent. Sometime in the late morning, I awoke to find a mama bear and two cubs prowling around my camp. Even though I had no odoriferous food such as fish or meat, I did have bread and other items in the truck cab. I'm sure the fish smell still lingered. After a half hour or so, they wandered off to find better pickings.

By the time the bears left, daylight was seeping over the horizon. I suddenly had a powerful hankering for more trout. I decided I would sneak up the creek and fish some more. I took my sawed-off pump 16 gauge (registered and legal length) with me just in case mama bear decided to help me fish. Apparently, the morning mist was conducive to good fishing because I caught ten, kept the six biggest ones and threw the four smaller ones back in the creek. As I walked back to my campsite, I realized if Mr. Warden showed up again, he wouldn't buy my story a second time. I remembered seeing a sign for fishing license at a store about twenty miles back. I hid the fish and headed out. As an out-of-state resident, I ended up paying three times the regular fee. Back at the camp, I retrieved my fish, cleaned them and started cooking. The smell was so powerful I thought I would starve before I got them cooked to perfection.

I stood my shotgun where I could reach it and started eating. By the third bite, I heard a truck coming. I knew who it was. He parked, got out and walked over.

"That shotgun registered?" he asked.

"Sure is," I replied. He whipped out a tape measure, walked over and measured the barrel. Satisfied that the length was legal, he stared at my fish.

"I suppose you bought these in Virginia, too," he said.

"No sir," I said. "I caught them in the creek." I pulled the license out of my pocket and handed it to him. He scanned it quickly and handed it back.

"Sure smells like the same fish you had last night," he said.

"I suppose all trout smell alike," I replied politely. "Would you like some?" I asked. "I have more than I can eat."

I could tell he was salivating. "Okay," he said. "I'll see if you can cook."

I put two nice ones on a plate with several hush puppies and handed it to him. He sat down in my other chair and started eating. I offered him some coffee and he accepted. We finished about the same time. He went to the creek and rinsed his plate, fork and cup. He placed them on my camping table.

"You're a good cook," he said and headed for his truck. He turned and looked at me. "Next time, you'd better pay more attention to the trout stamp on your license. Trout season doesn't start until midnight." He jumped in his truck and drove off.

The Lost Art of Still-Hunting

There was a time in my life when I knew exactly what I wanted to be, and that was a forest ranger. By the time I finished high school, my goal had eluded me, and I'm not sure why. I blamed it on financial considerations, but I had other goals as well. I couldn't be a ranger without going to college, and I had about two cents to my name when I graduated high school. I took the easy way out and joined the Navy. From that point, I never looked back, and I never considered forestry again. At least not for a profession.

In short, it turned out to be an avocation instead of a vocation. I was born loving the forests. Sometimes, I like to do things city folk would consider nutty. For example, I like to go out in the woods, find a nice quiet spot and just sit, watching and listening to nature. Native-Americans had a phrase in their vocabulary called "still- hunting." *(No, this is not what the revenuers did to locate grandpa's beverage production system.)*

Still-hunting was a phrase given to a method of hunting that was practical, unique and successful for Indian people before modern weapons were invented. Before he actually took to the field, the hunter would cleanse himself by fasting for about three days. This reduced his body odor significantly. Now, there are two types of body odor. One we can smell that causes us to bathe and the other type that animals can smell. The latter is the one the hunter wanted to reduce to near zero.

Secondly, the hunter would place himself in a good location where he knew his prey would likely be found. He would then sit or lie perfectly still, for hours if need be. Now the hunter had achieved two out of three objectives. The animals couldn't smell him, and after he sat long enough, they couldn't see him; that is, because he didn't move, they didn't consider him a threat and would ignore him. His third objective, of course, was to kill the animal, which he usually did.

When I was on a walkabout up in Montana a few years ago, I happened up on three Blackfoot Indians with whom I pitched several games of horseshoes. *(Blackfoot Indians don't like the plural, Blackfeet.)* They were amazed I knew about still-hunting. They had never actually done it themselves, but their grandfathers had told them numerous stories about the old hunting method. They knew quite a bit about the subject. I have talked to and e-mailed several Eastern Band Cherokee, and I can't find anyone who has knowledge of this ancient skill. It may be the older

Cherokee have not passed it on, and it may be I have talked to the wrong people.

Now, the point of all this is I like to still-hunt, but I don't kill the animals; I just observe them. I have actually tried this method and found it works. The technique is not an easy one, and it taught me to empathize with the long dead Indian hunters who did it in order to eat.

First of all, fasting for three days is extremely difficult, especially for those of us who have never missed a square meal in our lives except by choice. It's my understanding Indian people often went hungry in hard times, especially in winter. So it may be possible fasting was not as hard for an Indian hunter quite simply because he was used to it. Be that as it may, my stomach thought my throat had been cut for the entire three days. All I could think about was food, food, food. Even so, I was able to force myself not to eat. I did drink lots of water, and as I understand it, so did the Indian hunter.

The second part was also difficult; that is, sitting in one spot for a long time. About two hours was the best I could manage; so in some sense, I was more successful at fasting than sitting still. The Indian youth was taught at a very young age to lie on the ground almost motionless for hours on end...no moving to get more comfortable, no nose scratching and no sneezing or coughing. I found as soon as I tried to sit still (*I didn't lie on the ground*), my nose would start itching. I knew this in advance, and I would practice not scratching my nose for as long as I could stand it.

Now in a way, this sounds like self-punishment.

For someone like myself who is just doing it to find out what it's like, I suppose it is. For the Indian hunter, it was an entirely different matter. A successful hunt could mean the difference between eating and starving for an entire winter for a whole group of people.

In my case, I found a good spot in a secluded area on Wayah Bald. I was amazed to find that, after a while, the animals did ignore me. A rabbit, a fox and three deer walked right by me. Two wild turkeys almost walked over me. A few birds pecked at seeds almost within arms reach, but unlike Saint Francis of Assisi, I didn't hold out my hands for them to sit on. After all, who wants to be laughed at by a bunch of birds? I hate to admit it, but I scratched my nose a couple of times even though I did it very slowly.

Something else came into play I didn't expect. I found I was much more attuned to sounds of the forest than at any other time, probably because I sat still and had nothing else to do. Of course, there was a myriad of bird calls, a pheasant thrumming off in the distance, a whip-poor-will, crows, woodpeckers, hawks and even insects. At one point, I heard something snuffing, but I think it was a wild hog and not a bear. Had a bear come along, I don't think I would have had the nerve to sit still while he passed by. For sure, I wouldn't have scratched my nose, no matter how bad it itched.

Directly above and just in front of me, an owl sat on the limb of an oak tree. He *(or she)* was almost the color of the tree. He sat motionless with one exception. Every so often, he would move his head around like the periscope on a submarine. Suddenly, he flew off the limb, sailed silently out of view and returned in a few seconds with a ground mouse in his beak. He flew back to his same spot, where he devoured the poor squeaking mouse in one gulp.

As I said, I wasn't trying to kill anything; I was just observing. While I sat there, I figured out why my ancestors learned to hunt with a pack of dogs. It was a whole lot easier than using the self-discipline required to still-hunt. The dogs did all the work, and the hunter reaped the benefits. If the dogs were lucky, they were given a left over bone or two.

One of my dreams was to walk the Appalachian Trail when I retired. Unfortunately, I now have two bad knees, so a 2175 mile trek is probably out of the question. Instead, I have set my sights on walking the Blue Ridge Parkway. I figure I can make the 470 miles in about two month or less. Then again, I may just drive it and camp out. That way, I can dine on Moon Pies instead of granola bars and powdered soup. I might fast between Moon Pies, but I doubt it. And I'll scratch my nose every time it itches.

Gun Shy

S ince I happened to be in the neighborhood, more or less, I decided to stop off and visit my cousin, Mort, in Flat Lick, Kentucky. For those of you who don't know where Flat Lick is, it's probably because you're not coon hunters. Mort's real name is Throckmorton, but don't call him that unless you want a fat lip. He's very touchy about his name and apparently for good reason. His mama named him that when she found out his pappy was from Throck-morton, Texas. The story goes his daddy took one look at Mort and caught the Greyhound bus back to the Lone Star State. He was never heard from again.

So Mort grew up under the wing of his Uncle Jake who owned the finest coon dogs in Knox County. And believe me, there's a lot of coon dogs there. It's been said there are two coon dogs for every person in that neck of the woods. If that story is true, this equates to about 60,000 coon dogs penned up in some

6,000 dog lots. Now, that's a lot of dog...uh never mind.

As luck would have it, I found Mort sitting on the porch surrounded by several redbone coon hounds. He had an earthenware jug parked near his left elbow and a puppy in his lap. The mother hovered nearby, anxiously awaiting the return of her offspring. Mort showed no sign of releasing the pup. I reached the bottom step before he realized I was there.

"Hi Mort," I said, "How ya doing?" He looked at me rather sadly.

"Not so hot, Roy," he said. I sat down and leaned my back against the porch post opposite Mort.

"What's the problem?" I asked. "You look like you lost your best friend."

He stared at me for a moment, wondering if he should let me in on the secret. I waited patiently. Finally, he spoke. "My best dog, Claire, has turned gun shy."

"In what way?" I asked, not sure I wanted to get involved in what seemed like a silly problem.

"Every time she sees a gun, she tries to run off."

"You got any idea what caused her to get that way?"

"Not a clue," he moaned.

"Oh, come on, Mort, it can't be that bad."

"Is too!" he sighed. "One day she was fine and the next day she was a coward. When she runs off, the rest of my dogs follow her."

I gave it some thought. "Maybe you should just retire her," I suggested.

"Are you kiddin' me?" he said. "I need her

tonight. Me and the boys are going after that big coon up in Hennessy Cove."

"Why don't you just leave your guns at home," I ventured. "After all, you're not going to eat the coon. Why not just leave it in the tree?"

Mort looked at me like I had committed a capital offense. "You can't go coon huntin' without a gun," he said. "It ain't natural."

I stared at him for a moment. "Just do it like they do in Mississippi," I advised. "When you get the coon treed, climb up and throw it down to the dogs."

He looked at me like I had just invented Velcro.

"Yeah," he said, "Why not. I've always been a good climber." Having made a decision, he perked up immediately. "You going with us, ain't cha?"

"I wouldn't miss it for the world."

After a delicious supper of cornbread, creasy greens and wild yams cooked up by Mort's wife, Cora Lee, we loaded up the dogs and headed out. We met his buddies at the end of Lick Branch Road. They had enough redbone coonhounds between them to take down a herd of buffalo. The dogs milled around the trucks nervous and anxious to get started. Somebody whistled and the dogs headed up an old logging road with Claire in front. The men dropped the tailgates on their trucks and sat on them. While they waited for that special baying from the dogs, they passed around a pint jar of Kentucky homemade. About halfway into the second jar, the baying changed to a deep mellow tone. They all jumped up and headed up the road.

Since I had ridden over with Mort, I followed him. After a couple hundred yards, they all turned left into the woods in the direction of the baying. They sounded like a herd of wild hogs crashing through the underbrush. They ran on like a covey of marathon runners. Since I had to strain to keep up, they were obviously in better shape than I, but then they had several ounces of liquid energizer coursing through their bloodstream.

Just about the time I was ready to give up, we came upon a huge beech tree. In the bright moon-light, I could hear and see the dogs yapping, baying and milling around. Five men stood under the canopy trying to locate the coon by flashlight. Finally one of them yelled out, "There he is; sittin' on that big limb."

Suddenly, a big man by the name of Arley spoke in a loud voice. "Okay, Mort, leaving our guns at home was your idée. Climb up there and git'em."

Mort glanced over at me and then walked over to the tree. By jumping, he grabbed the first limb and pulled himself up. He went up through the branches like a monkey. The other four kept their lights trained on the coon so Mort could find him. The coon was hunkered down way out on a big branch. Mort crawled slowly toward him.

Just as he made a grab for the coon, the limb broke. Down came limb, Mort and coon. Mort yelled loud enough to be heard in Flat Lick. He and the coon hit the ground at the same time with Mort on top. Everybody rushed over. Both man and coon were still.

Finally, Arley bent down and shook Mort by the shoulder. "You alive, Mort?" he asked.

"I think I'm dead," Mort said.

"You ain't dead," a redheaded guy named Rudy

insisted. "If you wuz, you couldn't talk."

Mort rolled over slowly. "I think my back's busted," he complained.

"See if you can stand up," I suggested. Slowly he rose on his feet. As he did so, the dogs gathered around the coon sniffing at it. Satisfied that it was dead, they lost interest. Men and dogs gathered around Mort. Just then, the coon jumped up and ran off into the woods. After a couple seconds delay, the dogs took off in hot pursuit. "Well, I'll be danged," Mort said. "That's the first time I've ever seen a coon play possum."

Although nothing was broken, Mort had multiple bruises and lacerations as a result of his fall out of the beech tree. The coon had been knocked unconscious when Mort landed on top of him. Recovering from his stupor, the coon had made a successful dash for the underbrush. The dogs, thinking he was dead, had ignored him, giving him time to make his escape.

Now, they were in full pursuit again, their baying telling the hunters their whereabouts. Everybody stood there wondering what to do. The dogs, or maybe I should say the coon, made up their minds for them. I wasn't sure how they knew this particular coon was the one that had eluded them for years, but they were sure this was the one. They had even named him "Old Tricky," indicating that he was as smart as a fox.

In a few minutes, the lead dog, Claire, notified the world that her prey had been treed again by changing the tone of her baying.

From the sound of it, they weren't that far away, but Mort was too hurt to give chase. I told the others

I would stay with him so they could continue their hunt, but they weren't about to let Mort off the hook.

Arley and Rudy took him by the arms. "Come on Mort," Arley said. "We'll help you up the mountain. Atter all, it's yer hunt. You have first rights to that big coon. You been chasing him for three years now."

"Forgit it, Arley," Mort said. "I ain't climbin' no more trees tonight. I ain't able."

"I know that, Mort," Arley said. "I'm goin' to do the climbing fur ya."

"Arley," Mort said, "You couldn't climb up on a mule, let alone a big tree."

"Just hide and watch," Arley snarled. "I'll go up after that (expletive deleted) coon."

So off they went, part dragging, part pushing Mort through the woods. I walked to their side waving the light back and forth so they could see. We finally located the dogs milling around a hickory tree. Claire stood with her hind legs on the ground and her front paws against the tree, and she was howling and baying something fierce. Arley and Rudy leaned Mort against a tree and walked over for a better look. This time, they couldn't spot the coon with the flashlight. "Durn his hide," Arley said, "He's all the way in the top."

"If you can't see him, how do you know?" I asked.

"That's the only place he can be," Arley said. "These dogs know he's up there and that's good enough for me." He looked over at me. "You're tall and slim, why don't you go up and get him."

"Not a chance," I said. "I just came along for the

entertainment. Besides, my old daddy always said he didn't care how high he got just as long as he could keep one foot on the ground. That's my sentiments exactly."

Finally, Rudy volunteered to go up. He studied the tree for a moment and then jumped up and grabbed a limb. The limb broke, dropping him on his backside in the leaves.

"Dipstick," Mort said. "Ya gotta grab a limb that's big enough to hold ya."

This started an argument, and the other two guys; Ralph and Chester, brothers, I learned later, jumped in and broke it up. Then, each of them held one of Rudy's feet and lifted him up to a bigger limb. He looked like a walrus trying to work itself up on a beach. It actually pained me to watch.

Even so, he was soon out of sight. As he neared the top, the tree began to lean. The supple hickory didn't break but continued to bend under Rudy's weight. Now, the limbs were touching a big oak next to it, and unknown to Rudy, the coon swapped trees. I only knew that because I saw it jump against the backdrop of the moon.

By this time, Rudy was cussing like a shrimp boat captain and trying to climb back down the tree. I hollered at Rudy and the others and told them the coon was on the move again. The coon disappeared like a will-of-the-wisp. Rudy finally reached the ground and men and dogs started milling around trying to pick up the scent.

Gun shy or not, Claire quickly proved her worth by picking up the scent again. Now, we were off and running, downhill this time. The raccoon must have realized the boys were thirsty again because it ran between the trucks, crossed a log over the creek and headed across the next ridge.

Naturally, they all had to stop and enjoy the fruits of the corn before they started out again. With several stiff drinks from the fruit jar, Mort was now moving better; albeit, a little wobbly.

On the trail again, Arley tried to walk across the log and fell into the creek. The rest of us waded the creek and headed up the hill toward the sound of the dogs. Back down the other side, we crossed a set of railroad tracks into a low lying area filled with sumac and sycamore trees. In a few minutes, the dogs had the coon treed again.

We helped Arley onto a big limb and up he went. It was obvious he could climb better than Mort thought he could. He disappeared in the foliage and everything was quiet for a couple minutes.

Suddenly Arley started yelling and we heard hissing, growling and squalling. "That ain't no coon," one of the brothers said.

"What's going on up there, Arley?" Mort called up.

"There's an (expletive deleted) bobcat up here," he called down. "Somebody shoot the (expletive deleted) thing."

Rudy cupped his hands around his mouth and hollered back. "We ain't got no guns, Arley!"

More racket and I could hear Arley climbing down. I could see the bobcat following him.

"Jump, Arley," Chester called up.

"You crazy (expletive deleted)," Arley yelled, "I'm still thirty feet off the ground."

The bobcat gave one last attempt to claw Arley and then started back up. At about ten feet, Arley jumped, landed hard and rolled into a bunch of dogs. "I'm going to kill every one of these (expletive deleted) dogs," he bellowed.

It was now obvious that the night's fun was over. Back at the trucks, the boys all took their wet shoes off and sat on the tailgates polishing off the rest of their panther's breath.

On the way back to Mort's house, I drove, despite his objections. Cora Lee had biscuits and gravy on the stove and I had my usual three helpings. Mort said he wasn't hungry.

I said good-bye and as I crossed the porch, I saw that Mort was just finishing a hand painted sign.

"For sale. Gun shy coon hound. Doesn't know the difference between a coon and a bobcat. $2.00 or best offer."

The Missing Possum

Jerry Dale and Billie Ray had been best friends for many years. They both lived on their respective farms near Mortimer on the upper end of John's River. They both dropped out of school together on the same day. Miss Mills, ninth grade teacher, had chastised them both for not having their homework. They stood up together and walked out of the school never to return. Each got a job in Ab Carswell's sawmill. They did good work and Ab liked them, so they stayed on. Ab said on many occasions that they were so close one couldn't separate them with a peavey.

Despite their rough and tumble appearance, they caused no trouble and it was generally known they were more than willing to help anyone in time of need. They didn't drink or smoke and they rarely cursed. Of course, their favorite pastime was coon hunting. At any given time, they had upwards of a dozen redbone coonhounds between them.

At age 23, Jerry Dale married Geraldine Bigalow and a few months later, Billie Ray married her sister, Skylene. Both men turned out to be good husbands. They dutifully turned their paychecks over to their wives to buy food, clothing and other necessities. They did have one failing for which there seemed to be no cure. They went coon hunting every Saturday night, usually returning in time to go to church on Sunday morning.

Of course, they slept through Reverend Bryant's sermons because they had been up most of the night. But at least, their wives got to hear Brother Bryant's message. A few years later, Ab Carswell decided to retire, and he sold his sawmill to Jerry Dale and Billie Ray and allowed them to pay it off in monthly installments. By managing their money frugally, they were able to build two houses a quarter-mile from each other overlooking Craig Creek.

Their sawmill prospered and they expanded by adding a new saw line, an automatic offloader and a drying kiln. They knew little about bookkeeping, taxes and government regulations but Geraldine and Skylene did. The four of them actually made a cohesive team, and before long, they were making a good living. Despite their success, one thing remained constant. Come Saturday afternoon, Jerry and Billie began preparations for their weekly coon hunt. The only thing that had changed was their new trucks and fancy dog boxes to haul the hounds to the hunt.

And of course, they upgraded from redbones to Treeing Walkers. In addition to being superb coon dogs, the Walkers were much better family dogs, now that Jerry Dale had two kids and Billie Ray had three.

As they had done for many years now, they loaded the dogs into Jerry Dale's truck and headed out. They found an old forest service road just off Brown Mountain Beach Road. The dogs were more than happy to hit the hunting trail. The lead dog, Blizzard, hit the ground running and disappeared around a curve in the road. Jerry Dale and Billie Ray followed until the road ran out. There they stopped and waited for that special baying that would tell them the dogs had treed a coon. When they finally heard it, they realized the dogs were somewhere on the backside of Brown Mountain.

They headed out, working their way through underbrush, laurel thickets and sumac. As they walked, fog began to roll in. Soon, they couldn't see ten feet in front of them. "Did you check the weather, Billie Ray?" Jerry Dale asked.

"Naw," Billie Ray replied."I thought you did."

They continued to fight their way through the dark and fog and soon, it started to rain. "Sure was nice weather when we left," Billy Ray opined.

"Yeah, well, it ain't now," Jerry Dale stated authoritatively.

They continued to work their way toward the sound of the dogs. Then suddenly, the baying stopped. After about an hour, they heard the distinct baying of Blizzard. This time, the sound was coming from the direction of Maple Mountain.

"Stupid dogs," Jerry Dale said. "Now they're lost."

Billie Ray stared at him in the dark. "Well, Jerry

Dale, we ain't exactly found."

Finally, they could no longer hear the dogs at all. After another hour, they gave up. They shone their light around and saw a recess in a rock cliff that was deep enough for them to get under. They napped off and on until morning light began to seep across the mountain. Just as they were getting ready to leave, a pair of possums came in for their day's sleep.

"Might as well kill'em and take'em with us," Billie Ray said. "We need something to show for our night's work."

Somewhere along the way, they had lost their snacks and now they were famished. They debated about whether to cook one of the critters but gave up the idea because it would be too much work. They headed out, carrying their possums by their tails. In an hour or so, the fog lifted. They continued to walk, not knowing where they were. They tried to use the morning sun as a guide. In another couple of hours, as they topped a ridge, they saw a small church below them. They didn't recognize it but they knew services should be about to begin. In back of the church, they hid their possums behind a stump and walked to the front door hoping to get directions.

The beginning hymns had just started so they had no choice but to sit down in the back pew until the service was over. The preacher gave a fiery sermon on Jesus turning water into wine. At last, he began encouraging those still lost to come down to the altar and be saved. After several calls, no one had still come down.

Finally he said, "This service is not over until at least

one soul comes down." With stomachs rumbling, Billy Ray and Jerry Dale stood up and walked down the aisle.

"God bless you, brothers, what is your confession?"

"We're lost," Billie Ray said.

"I know that," the preacher said, "I'm here to help you."

"Good," Jerry Dale said, "Can you tell us how to get to Mortimer?"

The preacher, now confused, asked, "What do you want to know that for?"

"We want to go home," Billie Ray said. "We're hungry."

"You're hungry for the word?"

"Naw," Jerry Dean said. "We're starved, we want to eat breakfast."

Realizing he wasn't getting anywhere, the preacher decided to try another approach. "The ladies in the fellowship hall are making chicken pot pie; do you mean you want to eat with us?"

"We'd love to," they both chimed in at the same time. Out in the fellowship hall, Jerry Dean and Billie Ray each had two helpings of the chicken pot pie. While they ate, one of the members told them they were at the Collettsville Missionary Baptist Church and offered to give them a ride back to their truck. Not wanting to leave their possums, they went back to the stump to collect them. They were gone. After searching the perimeter around the stump with no luck, it dawned on them what had happened. Billie Ray looked at Jerry Dean and said, "Well, I reckon if the

Lord can turn water into wine, he can turn possum into chicken."

Bear Hunting in Bergoo

My old Navy buddy, Riley Jackson, called me on Saturday morning. I hadn't talked to him in at least ten years.

"Guess who?" he said. So we played guessing games for a couple minutes. I figured it out before he told me.

"So, how are things in the wilds of West Virginia?" I asked.

"Not bad, Cuz," he replied. Riley calls everybody Cuz; at least he does if he likes them. Unfortunately, I can't print what he calls people he doesn't like. I couldn't remember the name of the community where he lived, but I remembered the population was something like 75.

"Tell me the name of the place where you live," I said. "It just doesn't stick to my ribs."

He laughed. "It's Bergoo, Cuz," he replied.

We chatted a little more. Finally I asked, "Did you call me for any particular reason, Riley?" I could almost hear the wheels grinding.

"Well," he said, mainly I don't want us to lose touch with each other. We went through a lot together."

I chuckled at that. "We sure did," I said. "A lot of blondes, brunettes and redheads."

"Aw," he answered. "It tweren't that good,"

"I'm just kidding you, Riley," I interjected. "Ya kin call me Rile," he said. "Everybody else does."

After another ten minutes of conversation, mostly him talking, he finally got around to telling me why he really called. "Bear hunting season starts tomorrow," he said. "Me, Reuben, Ralph, Roscoe, Ryan and Razor are going bear huntin' and I just thought you might want to go along. We kin also swap stories about old times while yer here."

I sorted through the list of names while he continued talking. "Wait a minute," I interrupted. "Who's Razor?" I could hear a female voice snicker in the background.

"She's my wife, Cuz." Just when I decided I wasn't going to ask him why he called her Razor, I did. "It's real simple," he replied. "You make her mad, she'll cut yer throat."

"I'll definitely remember that," I replied.
Mulling it over for a minute, I said, "Okay, I'm in. How do I get to Bergoo?" I waited a few seconds for the wheels to stop grinding.

"It's real simple," he replied. "You just find I-79 out of Charleston, jump off on U.S. 19 south and then turn onto Birch River Road. "It's about an hour as the crow flies, and three hours if the crow has to drive. Ya can't miss it."

Next morning, I headed out. As I continued driving on U.S.19, I couldn't find a sign that read, "Birch River Road," and it took me an hour to find someone who knew where it was. Next, I ended up somewhere in Monongahela National Forest and had to backtrack.

Four hours after I left Charleston, I drove into Bergoo. It took another hour to find Riley's place. I ended up in a graveled cul-de-sac. I sat in my car and stared at five houses in a semi-circle. Riley came walking down the middle driveway, also gravel. He grabbed my hand and shook it until I thought it would fall off. "It's great to see you, Cuz," he said.

"Who lives in the other houses?" I asked. Riley stuck two fingers in his mouth and whistled. Four men and a woman came walking down their respective driveways. I knew who they were; I just didn't know who was which, but I figured the woman was Razor.

The brothers shook my hand until I thought it would fall off. I figured that trait must run in the family. Razor was a hard-looking pretty woman if you know what I mean. She had beautiful blue eyes that matched the sky. She gave me a gentle handshake and I had a hard time picturing her as mean and vindictive. Still, I've been around and I know that looks can often be deceiving.

After all the greetings and handshakes were finished, I asked Riley when bear hunting would begin. "We'll head out at 4:00 a.m. in the morning," he replied.

"Is this a human operation only?" I asked. "Or do you have a bear dog?"

He looked at me like I was totally ignorant. "Nobody hunts bear without a bear dog," he replied. "Come with me, Cuz."

We walked around behind the houses. Apparently, they all shared the same dogs, cats and all other critters they owned including the cows grazing in the field above the houses. We walked up to a large fenced-in dog lot. There stood two of the biggest, meanest looking dogs I had ever seen.

"What in God's name are those things?" I asked. Riley grinned like a possum.

"They're Caucasians," he replied. "They sure don't look like people to me," I countered.

"Nah," he said. "They're Russian bear dogs. They come from the Caucasian Mountains."

I stared through the fence for a couple minutes. "How're you going to keep them from eating us?"

"They're really very gentle around people they know," he added.

"That's just my point," I said. "They don't know me from Adam's house cat. Do they have names?"

"The one there on the left is Ivan," he replied. "He weighs in at 240 lbs. The female is Anna. She's a mere 210 lbs."

He opened the gate and I prepared to run. He stepped inside and Ivan immediately jumped up and put his paws on Riley's shoulders. The dog suddenly licked him in the face with his ten-pound tongue. They cooed and billed for a couple minutes and then Ivan got down and Anna jumped up. They went through the same routine. Finally Riley turned and said, "Come on in Roy."

I stared at him like he'd lost it. "Not on your

life," I answered. "Oh, come on in," he said. "They won't hurt you."

"And who's going to stop them if they decide to?" I asked. "It would take three of you to hold one of them."

I finally decided to risk it and stepped inside the fence. Riley rubbed my hand with both of his hands and then told me to pet Ivan. I reached out slowly. The dog sniffed at my hand. I knew if he decided to bite, I would lose several fingers, if not the whole hand. Suddenly he ran his long tongue out and licked my arm. Then he jumped up and put his paws on my shoulders. I lost my balance and we went down in a heap. I rolled out from under the dog and slowly stood up.

"You done good, Roy," Riley said. "Ya now have a new friend. One word of advice, though. Don't come out here by yerself."

I figured that statement was almost too dumb to answer, but I did anyway. "There ain't enough money to get me in this fence by myself," I replied.

Riley laughed. "Aw, he said, "they're just big old pets."

4:00 a.m. next morning came way too early. A heavy fog had descended upon Bergoo, West Virginia.

"Time to rise and shine, Roy," Riley called out cheerfully.

I had brought clothing for the occasion. I dressed quickly and slipped on my waterproof boots. Riley already had the dogs loaded in the back of his long bed pickup with extended cab. I figured it would take a ten-acre field to turn the thing around. Razor had made a sack full of egg biscuits and a thermos of coffee that must have held two gallons. We all rode in the cab except Razor who rode in the back with Ivan and Anna.

"We can make room for her up here," I volunteered. I had no intention of riding in the back with the dogs.

"Nah," Riley said. "She likes to ride with the dogs. She gets them psyched up for the hunt."

Since none of them had told me, I asked why the other wives weren't along. Ralph spoke up first. "My wife said she'd starve before she'd go bear hunting."

That answered my question. When we ran out of road, Riley put the gears in "bulldog" and kept going. We stopped at the base of a cliff. Everybody piled out of the truck. Riley handed me a backpack and a 9 mm pistol with holster. "That's in case you git lost," he said.

I strapped on the holster. "I know you're left-handed," he said, "but if a booger gits after you, you'll learn to shoot with that right hand real quick."

I noticed nobody had a rifle. "What're you going to shoot the bear with?" I asked.

"We're not," Rueben replied. "That's what the dogs are for. Tomorrow, we'll hunt with guns and let the dogs rest. Our pistols are just for emergencies."

"Like when a bear is breathing down your neck," I quipped. Like Marines, they all took out their pistols and checked them to see if they were loaded.

When in Rome, do as the Romans do, I thought, so I removed my gun and checked it also. I noticed Razor checked hers more thoroughly than the rest did.

"Were you ever in the military," I asked her.

"Retired Army sniper," she replied. She didn't look old enough to be retired, but I had no reason to doubt her.

Razor brought the dogs out of the back of the truck. Their chains looked big enough to hold a moose.

"Aren't you going to turn them loose?" I asked.

"Not until we see a bear," she replied. We headed out along an old animal trail. They took turns holding the dogs. I asked why the dogs didn't bark.

"They've been trained not to," Roscoe answered. "Barking will spook the bears and we'll never find one."

After about two hours of climbing up and down hills, Anna suddenly started sniffing the ground and whining low in her throat. "Okay, boys," Razor suddenly exclaimed. "We're hot on the trail. Keep a sharp eye out for Smoky."

Somehow, that didn't set right with me. I had grown up looking at pictures of Smoky the Bear on mountain highways. "How do you know it's not the scent of a raccoon or a deer?" I asked.

"My pets have been trained since puppyhood just to track bear," she said.

The dogs stayed hot on the trail. We crossed the same creek about six times. I still wasn't convinced they were tracking a bear. Eventually, we came to a logged area and I saw a big black bear slipping through the underbrush. Ralph, who was holding on to Ivan's chain, suddenly reached forward and removed it from his collar. Razor did the same with

Anna. The dogs took off like a shot. I was amazed they still didn't bark. Everybody broke into a run.

After about five minutes, I heard loud growling and snarling. As I rounded a copse of trees, I saw the dogs grabbing at the bear, trying to get a permanent grip on him. He was big and strong and he was tough. Every time one of the dogs would close in, he would dash forward in a defensive maneuver aimed at killing or maiming his pursuers. As I stood, trying to catch my breath, I looked at Razor.

"Looks like the bear might just kill the dogs," I said.

"Just watch," she replied.

Suddenly, Anna dashed in and grabbed the bear by a hind leg. I could hear bones crack and I was fifty yards away. The bear went down, turned and tried to get Anna by the throat. That tactic was his downfall. Ivan dashed in from the other side and got a grip on the bear's neck. The bear rolled in an attempt to throw him off. Again, a mistake on the bear's part. Ivan suddenly turned loose and reattached his massive jaws on the lower part of the bear's throat. No matter what the bear did, he couldn't get Ivan loose from his throat. It became apparent he was weakening.

At that moment, I would've preferred that the bear be shot. Finally, the bear stopped struggling. The dogs turned him loose and sat looking up at their masters. I didn't realize they hadn't been fed yet until Ralph took two large pieces of meat out of his pack and threw it to them. They bolted their food down in about five seconds.

"Do you know how to field dress a bear, Roy?" Riley suddenly asked.

"Not a clue," I replied.

"Well, you're about to learn," he said.

The brothers gathered around and took hold of the bear's paws. From somewhere in her bag of paraphernalia, Razor whipped out a skinning knife and began separating the fur from the carcass. A surgeon couldn't have done better. Now, I understood the real reason why she was nicknamed "Razor." Meanwhile, Ralph removed several plastic bags from his pack. He held one of the bags while Razor stuffed the hide into it. Next, she split the carcass down the middle and removed the intestines and other unwanted organs. Most of that went to the Caucasians. They wolfed it down like they hadn't eaten in a week. When she finished that chore, she began dressing out the meat. As she progressed with her cutting, I decided she should be working as a meat cutter in a supermarket.

When she finished, they collectively guessed the meat at 200 lbs. They divided the meat into four bags. Including the hide, we all had one bag each which went into our packs. It was a long haul back to the truck carrying the extra weight.

Razor hooked the chains back on the monsters. Ralph and Reuben, the two biggest brothers, held the dogs.

Back at the house, they built a big fire under a homemade grill. The other wives came out and I finally was introduced. Meanwhile, Razor brought out her special bar-be-que sauce. Soon they were grilling bear steaks while she continually basted the meat.

We all sat down for a big meal. Much to my surprise, the food was really good.

As they ate, they talked about preparations for tomorrow's hunt. I really didn't want to go, but I had committed. It seemed to be important to Riley. After all, we had spent some good times together in San Diego and Key West. Oh well, I thought, at least I don't have to watch another vicious struggle between dogs and bear.

At 4:00 a.m., we headed out again; but this time, we drove along Bergoo Swamp Road to a place called Abb Run.

As we exited the truck, I realized nobody had a rifle but Razor. "How come you guys aren't carrying a gun?" I asked.

"No need to," Riley replied. "Razor's the sharp-shooter."

As it turned out, Abb Run was a hodge-podge of ridges and ravines. It was still dark, so we had to watch our step all the time. Just at daylight, we topped a ridge and stopped. There was a clearing where a forest fire had taken its toll on several hundred acres. We all got as comfortable as we could. Ralph took several pairs of binoculars out of his pack and passed them out. For two hours we sat quietly and watched the burned out area. I was getting bored.

"I see one," Roscoe suddenly blurted out. I pointed my binoculars in the direction he was pointing. Sure enough, a bear was working his way across the open space. Razor got into position. She sighted through the scope of her 30-06.

Suddenly, she raised her gun. "Too small," she

declared. "It's probably a yearling."

We all sat back down for more waiting and watching. I was getting cold despite my three layers of clothing. I saw the next bear first. He was a large one. I told Razor.

In a few seconds, she fired and the bear went down. We approached carefully, but it was dead. We went through the same routine as the day before. Skin, cut up and pack. Razor didn't carry meat because she had the 30-06. It was a tough slog back to the truck, but we made good time.

Back home, the brothers brought out a big iron pot and set it up in the back yard. The women made a big pot of bear stew. As I watched, I lost track of the ingredients. After they finished, they let it slow cook for four hours. By then, everyone was famished and we pitched in. The stew was delicious. And of course, there was hot cornbread to go with it.

I prepared to leave. "Ya gotta stay for our family gathering Saturday," Riley said. I had other plans for the rest of the week, but I agreed.

By the time we finished breakfast Saturday morning, pickups and vans were pulling in. Aunts, uncles, cousins, kids and grandkids piled out of vehicles.

"Are all these people related to you?" I asked Riley.

"Every one of 'em, cuz," he replied.

People brought food and even tables to put all the food on. Fortunately, the weather was good for a December day. The brothers built a huge bonfire in the middle of the cul-de-sac so those who were cold-natured could warm up from time-to-time.

Before long, there were ball games out in the field, horseshoe pitching contests and even a shooting competition down the road. Riley asked me if I wanted to be his partner for horseshoe pitching.

"I hope you're as good as you used to be," he whispered. I probably wasn't quite as good as I was in the past, but we won the competition. When the relatives began congratulating us, Riley gave me the credit.

"It took both of us to win," I told them.

Next, we went out to the field to see how the softball games were going. They were only playing three innings so that others would have a chance to play. I struck out the first time and hit a line drive just inside third base the second time. I made it to second base. The next player hit a high ball which the shortstop caught easily. Razor was up next and the opposing team booed good-naturedly. She sneaked a bunt which the pitcher and the shortstop missed and I made it into home. Still, our team lost, five to four.

From there, we walked down the road to where the shooting competition was to be held. They all bet quarters on who would place second. It took me a couple minutes to figure out why no one was betting on first. Razor won both rifle and pistol competition hands down. I didn't try pistol because I knew I probably couldn't hit the target. I didn't do too badly on rifle though. I figured twelfth place wasn't too bad. After all, there were twenty-two shooters.

About 2:00 p.m., someone called out lunch. About 75 people gathered around the tables. Riley's

Uncle Jack, a retired preacher, asked the blessing. Of course, the kids were fed first. After that, everyone got in line and talked excitedly about family and activities. I stood in line with Riley. "How often do your folks do this?" I asked.

"Every three months," Riley replied.

Clearly, the families were close. I hadn't seen one argument among adults. Of course, kids will be kids and a couple of them had to be separated occasionally. The food was typical mountain fare, my favorite in the entire world. Nothing was store-bought. Everything had been home-cooked. I sampled so many dishes I lost count. After the tables were cleared, several people gathered to play musical instruments and sing. The musicians were good and the singers harmonized gospel, blue grass and country. I was certainly impressed. They kept the bonfire going until 8:00 p.m. at which time the reunion ended. Uncle Jack said a blessing for the families.

After all the relatives left, Riley, Razor and I sat by the dying bonfire for a while. We agreed it had been a marvelous day.

"What's your first name?" I asked Razor.

"It's Jackie," she replied.

"So how'd you really get to be called Razor?"

She looked away for a moment. "About five years after I joined the Army, a tech sergeant assaulted me while I was stationed on the Rockpile (Thon Khe Tri, Vietnam). I cut him up pretty good. After that, my buddies started calling me Razor. The name stuck and followed me around for the rest of my career. In a way, it protected me."

They made a good couple, Riley and Razor. She had been married to the Army. He had married his childhood sweetheart while we were stationed in Key West. Five years later, she and their daughter were killed in a car wreck when a drunk came around a curve on the wrong side of the road. As one would expect, Riley was devastated. He never took women seriously after that until he met Razor. She was an unusual woman; tough, attractive and intelligent, and I could tell she loved him. I was glad both of them had finally found happiness.

After breakfast on Sunday morning, it was time to head out. Razor shook my hand and then decided to give me a big hug. Riley did the same.

"Come back after Christmas and we'll do it again," he said.

"I'd love to," I replied, "but I've used up my vacation for this year."

Razor looked at me with her penetrating blue eyes. "Don't let work steal your life; you need to live a little, too."

I hugged her again. "Good advice," I replied. I waved out the window just before I drove out of sight.

"It never ceases to amaze me," I thought. "Mountain people live life to the fullest regardless of their financial situation, and the Jackson families were certainly proof of that

CHAPTER SEVEN
Preachers and Sinners

Parents, Grandparents and the Bible

I was raised on beans, taters, cornbread and the King James Bible. Mom and Dad read the Bible daily, and sometimes one or the other would read it to me. Psalms, Ruth, Proverbs, Ecclesiastes and the Gospels were instrumental in my learning to read. Ecclesiastes was probably my favorite because it had a lot of wise sayings. I could pronounce it by the time I was four or five, but I still can't spell it. Both of my grandmothers also read the Bible frequently. My Grandma Emma would sit on the front porch in her rocking chair where the light was good and read. She always wore her high-button shoes outside. Grandma Rosa would sit on an old car seat on her front porch and read her Bible. Both my grandfathers died before I was born, but I'm told they were also frequent readers of the Bible. Ditto on my great-grandfathers. I have my Great-Grandfather Porter's Bible—it's one of my most prized possessions.

The purpose of this story is to share memories; it's not intended to offend anyone. I say this at the outset because there are at least fifty versions of the Bible. Some people believe in the literal interpretation of their particular version and others interpret it. Therefore, I'll stick to the facts as best I know how.

The history of the Baptist Church is murky; in part, because there are several different versions of the Baptist faith. I have traced my forefathers back to 1670, and I'm a ninth generation Baptist. Over the years, I have made friends with Methodists, Presbyterians, Lutherans, Episcopalians and Catholics. I also have a Jewish friend in Tel Aviv with whom I exchange e-mails. While I may or may not agree with them, I certainly respect their faith. My Dad said on many occasions that a lot of Baptists were going to be surprised when they got to heaven and found a whole bunch of people from other denominations and religions walking around.

Second Timothy 3:16, King James Version reads: "All scripture is given by inspiration of God and is profitable for doctrine, for reproof, for correction, for instruction in righteousness."

When it came to raising their children, my parents used this verse as their guideline for teaching and correcting. For major infractions, I got the end of a keen hickory across my back. For minor violations, Mom or Dad would often quote various scriptures from the Bible. In some ways, that was more effective than the whipping. As far as I know, all my aunts and uncles were raised on the same Biblical doctrine, and all sixty-two of my first cousins received their corrections in the same way with a few minor variations. As far as they were concerned, the Bible was the authority, and any other guideline took a backseat.

Naturally, one can't write a story about the Bible without mentioning the Ten Commandments. In Exodus, Chapters 19 and 20, God gave them to Moses on Mount Sinai. If a person did nothing else but observe these commandments, he or she would possess good character.

Now, our forefathers believed in the separation of church and state, and so do I. I think their intent was that no religious group should run the government. Even so, I don't think they meant for the Ten Commandments to be removed from public buildings. It grieves me deeply to see this happen. In the same vein, I would not want any religious group, including my own, to have control of Washington. We can see the results of that in countries like Iran.

It is unfortunate the Bible has been used throughout its history to justify all kinds of wars, killings, prejudices and bigotry. People have built an entire denomination on one or two verses of the Bible taken out of context. Wars have been fought, families destroyed and nations brought to ruin because of the way church and/or political leaders have interpreted the Bible. People have handled snakes, hunted ghosts, practiced polygamy, killed off entire populations and justified bigotry and hate to the extreme based on a few verses in the Bible.

Jesus clearly said in Mark 12:30-31, "And thou shalt love the Lord thy God with all thy heart, and with all thy soul, and with all thy mind, and with all thy strength: this is the first commandment. And the second is like, namely this, thou shalt love thy neighbor as thyself. There is no other commandment greater than these."

I think it's fair to say my life has been guided by my parents' and grandparents' teachings based on the King James Version of the Bible. Like everyone else, I have committed my fair share of sin, but I can say with certainty the straight and narrow was pointed out to me many times. If I end up in prison tomorrow, there's no way I could or would blame my parents. They gave a big chunk of their lives bringing up their children to be good citizens and good Christians. I tried to do the same with my children. Regardless of one's belief or denomination, the Bible is certainly a wonderful guide for teaching and rebuking if it is used properly. And like anything else in this life, if it's in the wrong hands for the wrong reasons, it can be a dangerous weapon. A good analogy is that two aspirins are good for many ills, but take a dozen and death will probably be the result. I believe my Mom and Dad used the Bible as it was intended. Because I have been subjected to a different environment than they were, I don't necessarily believe exactly as they did.

I know for a fact that my dad took issue with a couple of Grandpa Lorenzo's beliefs. For example, Granddad was a strict observer of the Sabbath. He insisted that Grandma Emma cook all of Sunday's meals on Saturday. The children weren't allowed to play at all on Sunday. They had to sit quietly all day. Dad said he would not subject his children to that, and he didn't. Now, this doesn't suggest that he believed in working on Sunday. One time, he came to visit me on a Sunday afternoon and found me digging a root out the bank by my driveway. He told me that I would have to replace it with my nose on judgment day. I put the pick away and invited him into the house. He wasn't bashful about telling me something he thought was wrong no matter how old I was at the time. He and Mom were wonderful parents, and I hope that I am worthy of their love and values.

Amen, Brother Ledbetter

U ncle Mortimer Ledbetter was a farmer, preacher and part-time evangelist. He pastored the Chestnut Hill Baptist Church just south of Bridge Creek Road near Tiger, Georgia, for thirty years. Back in those days, the only way to get to the church was to walk or stare at the rear end of a mule for the time it took to negotiate the rutty wagon track for three miles on Briar Patch Road. Uncle Mort rode his mule to church and carried his preaching clothes in a toe sack. Once there, he would go to the outhouse behind the church and change. There was only one difference between his preaching overalls and his work overalls. The preaching overalls had been freshly washed. The Service started at 11:00 a.m., but everyone knew Uncle Mort would wait until he was sure the last straggler had arrived.

Mort would stand in front of the church and greet everyone as they came in. He had learned from experience their offerings would usually be in the form of chickens, eggs or a slab of fatback meat. Whatever they brought him, he would stick in a sack which he tied to the back of his saddle. It didn't seem to bother him that a laying hen and a big slice of pork might be in the same sack.

When he felt comfortable everybody who was coming had arrived, he would walk up the old worn steps, close the rickety wooden doors and make his way down the aisle. He would greet everyone with a handshake until he came to his brother, Minter Ledbetter. Minter could neither hear nor speak, but he came to church every Sunday. Mort would hug him and then move on up the aisle. A few of the members joked that Minter was lucky because he couldn't hear Mort's sermons.

Mort never walked straight to the pulpit. He would go through the side door and come around behind the piano which had been donated to the church by Woodrow Rector. How Woodrow had paid for the piano was never questioned. Upon arrival at the podium, Mort would lay his old Bible across the top and then stare at the entrance to the church for an interminable amount of time. Meanwhile, the church members who hadn't fallen asleep would cough and fidget. When Mort was ready, he would clear his throat and begin in a slow, rambling monotone. Those who hadn't already fallen asleep would do so at that time. As the minutes passed, Mort would increase both the tempo and the volume of his sermon. One by one, those who were sleeping would wake up because things were beginning to get interesting. Before long, he would be preaching so loud nobody could sleep.

About the middle of his sermon, Mort would stop briefly, go to the side door and open it. It didn't matter if it was summer or winter, rain or shine. Mort's flock knew why he opened the door. There was a Mashburn family who lived within shouting distance of the church and they didn't attend.

After Mort returned to the pulpit, the volume of his sermon would double. Billy Bradford, who always sat on the back pew, swore on a clear day Mort could be heard two miles down the road. Mort's reasoning for opening the door was sound. He intended for the Mashburns to hear a weekly sermon whether they attended church or not.

Another story went around that Mort scared the Mashburn's hens so bad they wouldn't lay for two or three days. That story was based on the fact Eloise Mashburn never gathered her eggs before Wednesday. Mort never gave up and after about five years, the family showed up one morning for preaching. Asked why they had decided to come, Vernon Mashburn said he got tired of hearing half a sermon.

Now, everyone knew Mort sometimes misinterpreted the Bible. After thirty years of preaching, they had learned to ignore his occasional meanderings from the Good Book. Aunt Gertrude Satterwite had her own way of telling him when he strayed from the Scriptures. When Mort said something like, "In the beginning there was light but nobody could see it;" she would call out, "Amen, Brother Ledbetter."

Of course, Mort didn't get it. Thinking he had

been bragged on, he would ratchet up the volume a little more and push on to the next nugget of wisdom.

One Sunday morning, Mort forgot to go to the outhouse and change into his clean overalls. At the height of his sermon, Gertrude called out, "Tell'em that cleanliness is next to Godliness, Preacher."

Woodrow Rector was always the first to get there. Most of the flock believed he came early to get his favorite seat in the Amen corner. When Mort got really wound up, Woodrow would begin to weep. When Mort stopped to catch his breath, Woody would say, "Amen, Brother Ledbetter. God bless you."

Woodrow had a still up in the holler at the head of Pine Ridge Creek. Everybody knew it except Reverend Ledbetter and the government. As soon as preaching was over, Woody was the first to go out the door. He would shake Mort's hand and then head for his mule. He would spend the rest of Sunday afternoon packing corn and sugar across Sumac Ridge and down to his manufacturing facility. In the dead of night, he would strap a dozen gallon jugs across his mule and meet up with his buyer in Lavonia. As far as anyone knew, the revenuers never found him out.

At the ripe old age of 83, he was accidently shot in the leg by a hunter who mistook his mule for a deer. Woodrow believed to his dying day that his leg had saved his mule's life.

Now every adult in the church had been saved at least once. That didn't stop Mort from having a call to the altar at the end of his sermon. Everybody also understood they would have to sit on the hard pews until someone went down; otherwise, they would all be sitting there until dark. Woodrow Rector certainly held the record for the number of times any member went down. The other members would punch each other and point. They all knew Woodrow wanted to get to his cooking business. Once preaching was over, Mort would go out by the mules and wagons and say good-by to his flock. On the way home, he would give the tithes he had received to those in need, usually a widow or a family with a long-term illness.

When it came to revivals, Mort had few equals. He would ride his mule fifty miles and sleep in the church where revival was being held. He was always offered room and board but he refused, citing the Apostle Paul's hardships throughout his Missionary Journeys. It was well-known that Mort could scare a hard-bitten sinner into a week of sleepless nights. He never waivered in bringing lost souls to the Lord.

The years came and went, and Mort retired. The members all pitched in and bought him an old truck to ride around in. Afterwards, they selected a young preacher with a college education to replace him. They eventually built a new brick church a half-mile down the road from the old one. When Mort died, the funeral was held in the old church. The mourners overflowed into the church yard. The church members buried Mort on top of Cemetery Hill with a panoramic view of his beloved Mountains. They all pitched in and bought a big stone on which they had engraved; "Here lies Preacher Ledbetter; we all loved him so dear. He misquoted the Scriptures a time or two, but his messages were loud and clear."

Baptists, Bibles and Backsliders

My dad used to say that no two people believe exactly the same when it comes to religion. Mom and Dad were both devout Baptists, but they did disagree occasionally on certain points. I think it's fair to say that Dad was more of a thinker about his faith and Mom was more of a believer about her faith. Dad understood the Baptist Creed better than some Baptist preachers and he was very knowledgeable about the Bible, too. Not only did he read it, he studied it, thought about it, processed it through his mind and prayed about it. He loved to discuss religion with people, especially preachers. He would draw them into discussions about the concept of Election which many Baptists know little about. From there, he would move to Salvation, Grace and Last Things.

From time-to-time, Mormons and Seven-Day Adventists would turn up at the house. Most people would turn them away, but Dad would invite them in and argue Bible with them. I have seen him take on three or four at a time. After an hour or two, they would leave shaking their heads because they hadn't budged him an inch. In fact, I think he convinced one or two of them to see it his way.

Mom was very knowledgeable about the Bible, too. She had a lot of pet verses she had memorized, and she never tired of quoting them when she thought it was necessary. She wanted her kids to grow up to be good Christians and she spent many an hour praying for us and making sure that we were walking down the straight and narrow.

She and I did not always see eye-to-eye. We had a lot of vigorous discussions over the years. By the time I was twelve or so, I realized she was unshakeable in her beliefs, so I often argued with her just for the fun of it. For example, she never believed that Jesus and the Apostles drank wine. She was convinced that they drank grape juice. I don't know whether they did or not but I would argue they did. On one of my trips to Israel, I brought this up to my friend, Hezi Aspis. Hezi thought it was funny. "Wine has been around since the stone age," he said. "Jews have been fermenting grapes for at least 3000 years and probably longer. We drink orange juice, grapefruit juice and apple juice, but I don't know any Jews who drink grape juice. It seems such a waste."

I remember Dad and Mom talking quite a bit about backsliders. Most of the time, the conversation was about good Baptists who had fallen by the wayside; that is, they had resumed their old habits of sinning. Every so often, Dad would say something like,

"Old so and so got caught with another so and so's wife."

Mom would say, "Backsliders, that's what they are, backsliders. They've got to get right with the Lord."

This invariably led to a discussion about whether the Baptist Creed meant "once saved, always saved." Some people believe this and some don't. In addition to just being curious about what other people believed, Dad also liked to find out if people really knew what they believed or if they really understood their denomination's creed.

One point of the Creed he pondered about was whether people went directly to heaven when they died or if Jesus raised them on judgment day when He returned. He wondered a lot about this one and he searched the Bible and other people's minds looking for a definitive answer. He and Mom discussed this many times, but I don't think they ever came to a conclusion.

Dad often said that a lot of Baptists were going to be surprised when they got to heaven and found people from other denominations and religions there. As I understood it, he believed anyone who accepted Jesus as his/her Lord and Savior would go to Heaven. This included all Protestants and Catholics. Even so, he was unshakeable in his own Baptist faith until the day he died. He thought people who were dogmatic in their beliefs got hung up on little things too often and overlooked the important things and I'm in full agreement with that. Dad didn't have much education but he had an inquiring mind and he wanted to learn all he could about religion. I'm sure I inherited my inquisitiveness from him. My faiths and my beliefs are not the same as his and he knew this would be the case before I did.

I really had little experience with other faiths until I joined the Navy. There I met Episcopalians, Mormons, Catholics, Methodists, Presbyterians, Lutherans, Jews, agnostics and atheists. The guys in my radar shop were a pretty intelligent bunch and we often discussed religion and philosophy well into the night. We rarely argued and we learned to respect each other's beliefs. I learned there are people who truly believe concepts that are very different from my own. I learned many people truly believe things I consider to be false. People have died for every religion in the world at one time or another. What I consider to be true and right, others may not.

I know that science and religion are often at odds with each other. I know we are all a product of our environment and heredity and there's no getting around that. Most people believe what they believe because they learned it from their parents, family, teachers and friends. Few people ever sit down and honestly analyze what they believe. My dad taught me to do that. I have a mind to reason with and a heart to remember with and I'm comfortable with my beliefs. I really don't care whether someone else agrees with me or not, but like my dad, I'm willing to discuss it. In my mind's eye, I can still see Dad sitting in my den with his Bible open discussing and arguing good naturedly with a group of Mormons. I can still see Mom standing in front of her old wood stove singing "Give me that old time religion, Give me that old time religion, it was good for Paul and Silas, and it's good enough for me."

They both loved God and God loved them and that's good enough for me.

From Sinner to Saint

Uncle Parvis Beasley was a character in his own right. He was well liked by those who knew him, despite the fact he cussed like a longshoreman from daylight to dark. He liked to tell people he and Aunt Julie had been married all their lives. People were forever asking her how she put up with him. She would just smile and say the Lord looks after fools like Parv. Anyone who knew them well would tell you they got along like peaches and cream. In every respect except for his cussing, he treated her like she was a valuable porcelain doll. He cussed everything he came in contact with but her, and he had never once called her a bad name in thirty years of marriage.

Gertrude May, Aunt Julie's sister told everyone who would listen the reason he didn't cuss Julie was because of the big black iron skillet that hung by the old wood stove. Gertrude claimed Aunt Julie had beaned him with it the day after they got married. According to her, Uncle Parv cussed the preacher for charging fifty cents for the marriage ceremony.

If Gertrude told the truth, it was probably because Preacher May was their daddy.

Uncle Parv cussed with every sentence he uttered. His twin brother, Jarvis, said he learned to cuss like he did while he was a prisoner-of–war at Camp Chase near Columbus, Ohio. Uncle Parv didn't talk about it much but he did say the camp was so nasty that a self-respecting farmer wouldn't have kept his pigs there. The mere fact he survived the ordeal said a lot about his stamina and constitution. He would often say God didn't make (expletive deleted) Union officers and soldiers, Satan did. Someone once told him Rebel soldiers mistreated Union prisoners-of-war also. Uncle Parv's reply to that was one word, "good." When the war was over, he said he was simply turned loose and told to make his way home. The condition of his health wasn't good so he found a barn loft to sleep in and stole food at night until he got well enough to travel. He knew enough about geography to realize his home was due south so he kept the sun to his left all the way.

As he traveled south, winter was slipping up on him. By early November, he had worked his way out of Yankee territory. In late December, he came down with the chilblains. He stopped at a farm near Pikesville, Kentucky. To make a long story short, Julie lived on the farm with her father-in-law. She had met her first husband in North Carolina and he had taken her back to Pikesville. Three months later, he was killed in the Civil War. She became a widow at sixteen. She found Uncle Parv in the barn, too sick to travel. She nursed him back to health. When he got well enough to travel again, spring had come, and he rescued her from her in-laws and took her back to North Carolina with him.

Despite his cussing, he treated her well on the trip south, a different life than she had had with her in-laws. She said he was a perfect gentleman all the way. Upon arrival, he withheld his cussing long enough to ask Preacher May for her hand.

As it turned out, Parv was a good provider. His Uncle Artimus Beasley gave him ten acres and a mule as a wedding gift. Parvis worked from daylight to dark until his farm was paying well enough to support them. He and Julie never had children, but in those days, people were too polite to ask why. The real truth was they didn't want to hear him launch into a long string of cuss words when he told them it was none of their business.

Gertrude, who always had an answer for everything, told a close friend who told a close friend that the chilblains had taken Uncle Parv's ability to have children. The real truth was probably some other reason, but gossipers will be gossipers.

As Uncle Parv got older, he started sitting in the Amen corner of the Piney Knob Baptist Church. Much to everyone's surprise, he managed not to cuss in church. When Reverend Wikle got wound up, started walking back and forth across the pulpit and mopping his brow with a red handkerchief, Uncle Parv would

say, "Amen Brother Wikle, God Bless you."
Everyone in the church would hold their breath, fearing that Parv would launch into one of his cussing tirades, but he never did. As soon as he got out of sight of the church he reverted to his normal cussing self.

One day, Aunt Julie caught him in the barn loft reading the Bible. "Whatcha reading the Bible for, Parv?" she asked. "And why out here? I ain't never seen you read it before."

"Well, Julie," he replied, "I'm thinking about becoming a preacher." She stared him right in his baby blue eyes and said, "How ya gonna do that, Parv? Ain't no respecting church member gonna listen to a preacher cuss."

Parv mulled that over for a minute. "I reckon I'll just have to quit cussin' then."

As she started back down the ladder, she looked at him and said, "I'll believe it when I see it."

From that day forward, no one ever heard Parv cuss again. Some said he had had some kind of revelation. Gertrude said Julie had knocked some sense into him with her big black skillet.

As time passed, no one knew Reverend Wikle was giving Parv preaching lessons down by his still where no one could hear them. One warm sunny Sunday morning, the good Reverend announced he was going to retire and he would appreciate it if the membership would consider Parv for their preacher.

Of course most of them had their doubts but the very next Sunday, the Reverend announced that Parv would preach the sermon that day. Parv really put on a show, but it was a good show. When he started calling for sinners to go down to the altar, he scared Harley Barton so bad that he ran down the aisle. Agnes Barton had been trying to get him saved for thirty years. From that moment on, everyone knew Piney Knob Baptist Church had another fine preacher.

For once, Gertrude kept her opinions to herself and simply said that "God works in mysterious ways."

Little Country Church

In the years before my family moved to Burke County, we lived on Camp Branch, a section of Nantahala. We attended Union Hill Baptist Church. Today, it looks very much like it did in the 1940's except it has inside toilets and a shelter for church activities such as picnics and family reunions. It was established in 1892, and my great-grandparents, Mr. and Mrs. William C. Mason, were charter members.

We didn't have a car, so we walked to church. Mom and Dad would always check to see if Grandma Rosa had already started out. Most of the time, she had, but if not, we would walk with her. Sometimes, someone would come along and offer us a ride. Generally, it would be a pickup truck, and we would all crawl on the back. Amos and Flossie Grant lived just below my grandmother, and they had a logging truck. They had about twelve kids, and it was a squeeze to bum a ride with them. Even so, Amos could haul enough people to fill half of one side of the church.

My Aunt Etta and Aunt Frances lived a little farther down on Camp Branch Road. They had enough daughters between them to fill a small school bus. Often, we would stop and eat with one family or the other on the way back from church. Sometimes we kids would get pretty hungry because of the time required to run down a chicken, clean it and then cook it. Even so, Sunday dinners were always delicious, regardless of whose house and which cook.

Nantahala has produced some mighty fine preachers over the years. The one I remember best is Clint Grant. Now, Clint was not a shrinking violet when it came to preaching. He believed what he said and said what he believed. He would start out slow and easy, and as time passed, he would increase both the intensity and the volume. Clint knew his Bible, and he was not short on words. He could weave a sermon like an expert weaver making fine cloth. Church members often had to pay close attention to grasp the depth of his message. He would walk back and forth across the pulpit of Union Hill, shouting, waving his arms and espousing scripture, chapter after chapter. He knew how to make sin sound like a dirty word, and anyone who heard him knew that a sizeable portion of hellfire and brimstone would be served up on a platter of man's sinful nature. He hated sin and loved the sinner, and he made no bones about it. He had a way of getting his message across without offending, a trait that serves any preacher well.

I remember Dad saying one day at the dinner

table, "Clint can shuck the corn right down to the cob." Dad knew his Bible better than most, and he knew when a preacher erred on scripture. I don't remember him ever saying Clint was wrong. I do remember him pointing out a few errors made by other preachers.

I remember a particular funeral, but I don't remember who died. Clint said on several occasions the deceased was in heaven with Jesus. I know a lot of people were crying, so the deceased must have been well known and loved.

After a while, I started feeling bad because I wasn't crying, but I didn't have anything to cry about. At that age, I really didn't understand, but I knew I had to do something. When I was sure no one was watching, I stuck my finger in my mouth and rubbed it around my eyes to make it look like I had been crying. I must have done a pretty good job because my grandmother put her arms around my shoulders to comfort me.

Naturally, almost everyone went to the cemetery on the hill above the church. It overlooks the valley of Camp Branch. Some people got to ride, but a lot of them had to walk, and it is a half-mile hike, most of it uphill. Like most funerals, everyone would gather around for the preacher's final message. I remember one funeral that was conducted there in the winter. It was cold and windy. I was just coming to grips with what death was about. I thought about how cold it must be to be buried there on that windy hillside. I've been there many times since then, and I still think that.

Hershel Mason was also a long-term pastor of Union Hill. He spent many hours studying his Bible and preaching according to the scriptures.

I don't remember all the pastors, but Phillip Passmore, S.J. Waters and J.C. Day also preached many sermons there. Like the Apostle Paul, these good men worked outside jobs and ministered to their flock when they could.

Again, anything having to do with food, I remember well. I remember the "all day singings and dinner on the ground." Sometimes, people from other churches would come to sing. Occasionally, quartets from Bryson City, Andrews or Franklin would turn up. Mom and Dad stayed for the singing, and I stayed for the dinner. My sister, Joyce, was only two or three at the time, but she probably remembers being stuffed full of food by her aunts and cousins.

I wouldn't eat much of the meats and vegetables because I wanted to save room for dessert. My mouth waters when I think of the hot apple, cherry and peach pies, strawberry and blackberry cobblers, three and four layer home baked cakes with chocolate, vanilla and other delicious icings. The first lemon pie I ever ate was at one of those dinners. I kept sneaking back for more until my mom got after me for hogging it.

My grandmother and my mother both loved that church. Even after we moved away, Mom would attend every chance she got. She loved preaching, but she love singing more. Not many things got her total attention, but that did. She especially loved to go with members of her family. After she got home, she would continue to sing the songs she had heard. When she could, she would sit with one or more of her sisters. It was her wish her funeral be held there, and we made sure that happened.

A long serving pastor of Union Hill in recent years is Oscar Passmore. Oscar served in the Navy in World War II, and his ship was hit by a torpedo. That was the only bomb dropped by a Japanese dive bomber that went through the side of a ship and did not explode. Oscar was close enough to it, that if it had exploded, he would have been killed. I think God was saving him to be pastor of Union Hill.

I believe God has blessed that little church, but then, why wouldn't he? Some of his most faithful servants have attended there, many of them for sixty, seventy years or even longer. Of course, there are lots of little churches like Union Hill in Western North Carolina, and their members think their church is special also. And certainly they should, for many of them have given their life to it. Ask one of them, and they will be quick to tell you it isn't the building, but God's presence inside that makes all the difference.

The Last Supper

I sat at the kitchen table and stared at a picture of the Last Supper on the wall above the refrigerator. It was a copy of the famous painting by Leonardo da Vinci. It was probably the only one Mom had ever known, and she loved it. Dad wasn't into visual things as much as Mom. He read and studied his Bible a lot. He knew enough to be a preacher, but he said he wasn't called. He didn't care much for speaking to groups. He had built this house in 1946-47 with his own hands and Uncle John's help.

I sat on the bank and watched the horse pull the drag pan as they prepared the house place. It seemed to me that the horse went back and forth a thousand times. In the upper corner, Dad set a locust pillar about a foot long and sat on it. It was today's equivalent of a cornerstone. I was present when they placed the double two-by-eights across the pillars to make the rear sill. Plank by plank and nail by nail, they raised the house until the last shingles were laid across the top to make the ridge cap.

This was to be the home Mom loved best. It was just a plank structure, but it had character, and it still does. It was built with two hammers and two hand saws. A manual plane was used to take out a few of the rough spots. The spring was just above the house and the outhouse was on the hill away from the branch. There was no electricity. We ate, worked and studied by kerosene lamp. A wood stove sat in the living room for heat, and a wood cookstove sat in the corner of the kitchen for cooking and baking. Some of the best food I ever ate came from that stove, made with love by Mom for her family.

I took my baths behind it in an old washtub. On cold winter nights, we slept with quilts and blankets piled high to keep us warm. In the mornings, Dad started a fire and then broke ice out of the water bucket for water to start the coffee and make gravy. When he shook me to get up, I knew a hot breakfast awaited me. In good times, it was biscuits and gravy with eggs and bacon. In hard times, it was cornbread and squirrel gravy. I don't ever remember not enjoying it. Breakfast was my favorite meal then, and it is now. We lived there about two years, and then we moved to Valdese, NC. I was brokenhearted.

In the blink of an eye, sixty years passed, and memories scrolled across my brain like an old movie. Dad died twelve years before Mom did. When she died, I couldn't face throwing their things away in this old house. It was hard enough emptying out her apartment.

Now, here I sat, two years later, determined to

do what I couldn't do before. I continued to stare at the picture, and tears started streaming down my face. My grandson, Nathaniel, had gone out to the truck, and I didn't want him to see me until I regained my composure. Mom and Dad believed with all their hearts that they would go to be with Jesus when they died. It suddenly occurred to me that no real picture of Jesus exists in this world. I'm not sure one ever did. Even so, Leonardo did a good job. It was sufficient, and I was grateful that Mom and Dad had their Lord to guide them through their hard lives.

I prowled around the rooms, not sure what to do next. Finally, I started going through drawers and shelves. Mom was a pack rat, and I soon found that she had thrown nothing away. I found family pictures everywhere I looked; including my old Navy pictures I thought had disappeared years ago. Old pictures of her mom and sisters, friends and relatives lay about in every location.

I found a box to store them in and placed them one-by-one on top of each other. This task alone took hours. Nathaniel pitched in to help and soon had his own collection to add to mine. He looked at them studiously and asked a lot of questions. It seemed hours before I had all the pictures gathered together in a big box. Before placing the lid on top, I stared down into the box. Almost one hundred years of history stared back at me, unmoving, but alive nonetheless. I wondered where the time had gone, but then we all do that.

Both my grandmothers spoke to me from their pictures; loving mothers of impeccable integrity who had struggled and toiled to raise large families on little but beans and potatoes. And yet both had survived to old age, determined to beat back disease, hunger and pestilence. Epitomes of pioneer women, hardy, hardworking and religious. They went to their graves to meet their God and left their children to live in a better world, at least in the material sense.

And so it was with the next generation. Mom and Dad, my aunts and uncles, almost duplicates of their Godly parents. And finally to me, my sister, brother and my cousins who left that mountainous land for a better life and the opportunity to give our children more comfort and education. And now, generations down the road, my grandson sat wondering how people could live with so little and be happy.

"Happiness is much more than material comforts," I told him. "If these Godly people have taught you nothing else, I want you to remember that."

"I will Pop Pop," he said, and I felt the sincerity in his voice.

The next two hours were spent removing bed clothes to be laundered and old clothing to be thrown out. One by one, I packed them in boxes, and it seemed that ever item ripped a piece out of my heart. I forced myself to go on until I was satisfied I had done all I could. Nathaniel carried boxes to the truck and I went in to lock up. I sat back down at the kitchen table just for a moment. Again, I stared at the picture on the wall, and Jesus stared back at me.

That picture stays, I thought. In a way, it represented the crux of Mom and Dad's religious life. I wondered where the picture would be one hundred years from now. Probably gone and forgotten, I thought, but other pictures of the Lord's Supper will endure generation after generation. I reminded myself that a picture is only a representation, not the actual event.

Even so, its meaning speaks volumes. I remembered the old adage that a picture is worth a thousand words. Suddenly, I understood a picture of the Lord's Supper is priceless, not in market dollars but in human value. It had given me strength to do what I had come to do, and I suddenly felt better for having accomplished it. I knew Mom and Dad would understand. When I walked off the porch, I realized that someday Nathaniel and his brothers would participate in discarding my things. He knew that I knew, and we were both okay with that.

The Mystery of Wildcat Cove Cemetery

In 1970, I hired Jim Byers to drive the company van back and forth to Charlotte and to do other odd jobs. He was one of the hardest working and dedicated men I've ever met. Jim was born in McDowell County, West Virginia. He walked away from the coal mines a few days after the death of his wife. He drove down I-77 until he reached Mooresville, NC. When I hired Jim, he was in his early sixties. He made the best catfish stew I've ever tasted. He would invite me over and while we waited for the stew to cook, he would regale me with West Virginia stories. I wish I had written them down, but I still remember a few. Here's one of them. I hope I've done Jim's story justice.

Nobody knew where Wiley came from. One Sunday morning, he turned up on the back pew of Wildcat Cove Baptist Church. As it were, he was a small man, intelligent but somewhat timid. A few folks welcomed him and one or two asked where he was from.

"From Canada," he said, but he didn't sound Canadian. His accent was pure West Virginian. Some speculated he simply walked away from troubles at home. Others suspected he might be hiding out from the law. In any event, Wiley joined the church on his third visit. From that point on, he attended every service.

Somewhat true to his personality, he became a clerk at the general store. At age thirty, he allowed himself to be pushed into marrying his pastor's daughter, Agnes Blankenship. They had one child, a son. As it turned out, Agnes was a domineering woman who wanted Wiley to become a preacher like her father. She didn't like being married to a store clerk because she thought Wiley should be in a position of some importance. After five years of marriage and little peace at home, Wiley became a minister. The Reverend Thomas Blankenship had decided to retire, and both he and Agnes pushed to get Wiley the position.

As the months passed, Wiley turned out to be a good preacher. He was thorough and methodical and this gave him the ability to deliver a good sermon. Ironically, Wiley was called to preach some months after he began preaching. Agnes, of course, quickly became the matriarch of the church, and her pushy nature gave Wiley many cases of heartburn. As the years passed, it was clear the members loved him and despised Agnes. Ida Hughes, the community midwife for fifty years, was quoted as saying delivering Agnes had been her biggest mistake.

In the middle of May, in their tenth year of marriage, Agnes became ill. After several visits to a doctor in Bluefield, she was diagnosed with cancer. Three months later, she died. Wiley tried to appear as broken-hearted as he could. Even so, he decided as minister, it was his job to preach the eulogy. He stood straight and tall in the pulpit, looked heavenward and began:

"Lord," he prayed, "you know I've been your faithful servant these many years. I've never asked anything for myself. So, at this time, Lord, I ask you one small favor. I know Heaven is a mighty big place. It has to be to hold all the Christians who have ever lived and will live. So Lord, what I ask is for you give Agnes a special place in your magnificent Heaven as far away from my mansion as possible. Make it so far away that she can never find me. If you do that, Lord, I will be your faithful servant as long as I shall live."

Just as Wiley finished praying, he realized the church was unusually quiet. Fearing he might have offended someone, he looked up. Ida Hughes stood next to the pew where she had sat at almost every service since she became a member. At age 97, she supported herself with a cane in her left hand and the back of the pew with her right. Ida, a widow for thirty years, and the only living charter member of the church, commanded great respect from the membership. Wiley knew she wanted to say something important; at least it would be to her.

"Ida," Wiley asked gently, "would you like to speak?"

"Preacher," she said, "we want you to pray for us

too. I'll be gone a long time before you go, and I want to be there waiting to greet you." She turned loose of the pew so she could make her point. She waved her hand in a circle as she looked around the church and then back to Wiley. "Reverend," she said, "you're the best thing that ever happened to this church, and we want to be with you on your side of heaven. I believe I speak for all the members."

Without a word, every man, woman and child from the back pew to the Amen corner rose to their feet and gave Ida a standing ovation. It seemed un- usual behavior for a funeral, but Jim said it was true.

Jim said that Ida lived to the ripe old age of 103. She had been a charter member for eighty years. As the only midwife and no doctor, she had delivered everyone in the community between the age of thirty and eighty. At her funeral, every pew in the church was filled, and the churchyard was full to the drive- way. Wiley delivered the best eulogy in the history of his ministry, and the church was filled with crying and sobbing. He did not forget to pray for Ida would be on his side of heaven. The choir and the membership sang Ida's favorite song, Rock of Ages. They could be heard two miles away at Hefner's General Store.

A few weeks later, someone noticed fresh flowers appearing on Ida's grave at regular intervals. No one thought much about it since she had been friends with everyone in the community. As this continued into the winter months, people began to speculate. Where could flowers be coming from in the middle of winter? Many thought it was Wiley, but he said, "No, it isn't me." When the flowers continued into the spring, three of the deacons decided to hide out in the cemetery and put a stop to the speculation. At dusk, they conveniently located themselves behind three tombstones, but in plain view of Ida's grave. When the sun rose, they had seen no one else in the cemetery. And yet, when they walked to Ida's grave, flowers as fresh as the morning dew lay atop Ida's resting place. After the third try, they gave up the vigil and told everyone else an Angel was visiting the cemetery at night. Being good Christians, the members accepted that explanation.

The flowers continued for five years. One cold winter night, Wiley, the church's pastor for sixteen years, died of heart failure. Shortly after his funeral, someone noticed that the flowers on Ida's grave had stopped. Some of the more practical members believed Wiley had been doing it and just hadn't been caught. Others speculated that perhaps Wiley himself was an Angel. After all, he had just appeared out of nowhere, and no one ever knew his origin.

"To this day," Jim said, "no one has ever solved the mystery of Wildcat Cove Cemetery." Having already figured out the answer, I asked him if he had known Wiley.

"Yes," he said. "He was my father, the best any man could ever hope to have."

Snake, Snake, Where's the Snake

My Daddy and my Great-Uncle John were great storytellers. Of course, they never wrote any of them down and most of them have disappeared into that mysterious black hole called time. I do remember a few and occasionally I like to share them with others.

Now, both men were good Christians, but they didn't let that stop them from embellishing the truth once in a while. They both worked in wood camps around Western North Carolina for many years. Most of the time, there was no one around except the group of men who happened to be cutting wood at that particular place in time. Naturally, they would sit around the camp and tell stories. If it were cold weather, they would sit around the fire. Some of the stories were true, some of them were exaggerated and some of them were just plain fiction. But it didn't really matter, they were just entertaining each other anyway.

Dad usually went to church on Sunday regardless of where he was working, and he usually went to the nearest church. Now, he was a Baptist through and through. He believed everyone in the congregation should keep quiet except the preacher. He did make an exception for the Amen corner. So when he attended church of a different denomination, which he sometimes did, he liked to tell about how they worshipped differently from what he was normally accustomed to seeing and hearing. For example, he would tell about people talking in tongues, rolling on the floor or jumping benches.

On one occasion, he was working at a wood camp near Granite Falls, NC. He became friends with a local man, and a few weeks later, he invited Dad to go with him and his wife to church. As it turned out, that Sunday evening, they had a guest preacher from West Virginia who was a snake handler. Dad's friend, Willie, and his wife, Irene, usually sat in the front row on the right side. Dad rarely criticized anyone but he did say Irene was a rather large woman who was strong as a mule. About halfway into the service, the preacher brought his box of snakes out from behind the pulpit. Dad said he immediately got up and moved back about six rows. Willie and Irene stayed where they were.

As Dad watched, the preacher removed a large timber rattler from his collection of snakes. He held it up above his head and started citing Bible verses about taking up serpents and they wouldn't hurt true believers. Suddenly the preacher walked up to Irene and handed her the snake. Apparently, she was so shocked she took it in her hands. Suddenly, she realized she was holding a huge poisonous rattler. She screamed loudly and threw the snake up over her head, demonstrating for everyone that she wasn't a 90 pound weakling. The snake sailed up and back and landed on a rafter. It hung there; its body extended on both sides and its mouth open as it revealed two large fangs.

People on the right side of the church quickly lost their faith and began vacating the church immediately. It was a hot summer evening and the windows were open. There were no screens on the windows. Several people either climbed out or jumped through every window on the right side. The people sitting near the aisle went charging out the front door, running over each other as they went. A few of the ones in the middle jumped the pews as best they could. Dad took the path of least resistance and walked back up toward the front. After a couple minutes, the snake managed to pull itself up onto the rafter and started crawling toward the left side.

Of course, the people on the left side headed for the windows or the door. Shortly, everyone on that side was gone except one fellow, who had apparently fallen asleep. His wife, a woman named Etta, came back up the aisle and hollered at him to wake up. When he didn't respond, she yelled, "For God's sakes, Henry, wake up, there's a snake hanging over your head." Henry slept on. Just then, the snake slipped off the rafter and landed in Henry's lap. The sudden weight woke him up and he sat staring at the snake.

"Don't move, Henry," Etta called out. "Maybe the snake won't bite you." Just then, Henry started hyperventilating and passed out. Etta started yelling for someone to help him. Obviously she had no intention of risking her own neck in an attempted rescue.

A few people came back in and stood in the aisle wondering what to do. Meanwhile, the snake crawled out of Henry's lap, dropped down off the pew and started crawling across the floor. Everyone, including the snake handler, vacated the church, leaving Henry and the snake inside.

Apparently, the snake handling preacher had enough faith to hold a snake in his hands but he didn't want one around his feet. That was a different kind of trust. Outside, Etta was still trying to get someone to go inside and help poor Henry. Meanwhile, all the other members who hadn't left for home stood speculating what to do.

Dad said he walked down to the creek, took off his hat and filled it up with water. He carried the hat through the door, down the aisle and turned into Henry's pew. Of course, he watched for the snake every step of the way. He tilted his hat and poured the water on Henry's head in an attempt to bring him around. Suddenly Henry woke up and hollered out, "Dear God, now it's raining snakes," and passed out again. Dad shook him a time or two and then gave up. He went back outside and walked up to Etta.

"I'm sorry to say, Henry's still out," Dad told her.

She looked at him for a moment. "That's all right," she said. "Let the snake have him. He's too lazy to work anyway."

Enforcing the Word

J im Byers made the best catfish stew I've ever eaten. One afternoon, he invited me to partake of his delicious stew. I ate so much all I could do was sit in a comfortable rocker on the porch. Jim rocked for a little while, and I knew he was warming up for one of his stories he loved to tell me after dinner. Shortly, he slid his rocker around to face me and began.

"James McLean was jerked up by the hair of his head. Later in life, he said when he was growing up; his family was so poor the cat was afraid to come in the house for fear of being eaten. James was sixteen years-old when the last decade of the nineteenth century descended upon the southwestern Pennsylvania coalfields. Coal mining was still in its infancy when he picked up a shovel and walked into the Indian Creek Coal Mine near Saltlick, PA. By age seventeen, he was a big man, broad in the shoulders with arms as big as most men's legs. In addition to his six-foot, six-inch frame, he was strong and agile, making him a favorite of the mining foremen. For him, making the daily tonnage quota seemed easy. During lunch, often far underground, he and some of his friends would have contests to see who could lift the heaviest coal bucket loaded with coal. Soon, the contests became boring to James because he never lost.

"One Saturday afternoon, a traveling circus stopped in Saltlick. One of the sideshows was a boxing match featuring a winner-take-all. James watched with fascination as the circus boxer easily took down all challengers. The prize was ten dollars to anyone who could defeat the featured boxing champ. To James, that was a lot of money, given that two dollars was the most money he had ever had at one time.

"When the next call came, he climbed the ladder and stepped into the ring. When the reigning champ called him a dumb coal miner, James hit him quickly and decisively. The champ went down on his knees and then passed out on the mat. James had just made a month's pay in two minutes. Thinking the young miner had just been lucky; the promoter bet him five dollars that he couldn't take the champ down again.

"Even though he suffered some cuts and bruises, he took the champ out in the second round. The owner fired the champ and hired his challenger.

"James had never been more than twenty miles from home so the opportunity to travel excited him. At a stop in Williamsport, he met a tent preacher who converted him. He quit his good paying job and went to work for the preacher. It didn't take him long to figure out his new boss was a shyster. On his first payday, the preacher reneged on the amount he had promised to pay James, claiming he didn't have the money. Disgruntled and disillusioned, he took the preacher's strongbox which was concealed under the floorboards of the wagon and headed back to Saltlick.

"He began preaching to the miners when they had time to listen. Fearing James was stirring up trouble, the mine owners ordered him off their property. Refusing to take no for an answer, he used part of the money the phony preacher had stored in the strongbox and bought a small piece of property within sight of the mine entrance. He used the rest of the money to build a church.

"On the first Sunday after he opened the doors, two people attended. He preached his sermon just like he had a church full of people. Soon word got around and the pews began to fill up. One Saturday morning while he was cleaning the church, three so-called mining deputies showed up. They found him with broom in hand in front of the altar. They told him if he didn't close the church, they would beat him severely. He hit the speaker of the group across the head with the broom handle and then beat up the other two with his fists. He dragged them out of the church and threw them into the road.

"In a few months, the church had deacons, a choir and a piano. James recruited the Harmonites from Harmony, Pennsylvania, whom he had met in his travels, to sing and play at a company picnic on Saturday. The mine always ran a partial shift on that day. In the middle of the picnic, someone came running up and said there was a cave-in two-thirds of the way back in the mine. As it turned out, fifteen men were trapped inside. Every man who was at the picnic started digging. They knew it was a desperate effort but they had to try. James went to the mine foreman and asked him to get company men to help him dig. He told James there weren't any men available.

"Just after dark, with a sawed-off shotgun in hand, James walked through the back door of the home of Howard Braxton, President of Indian Creek Coal Mine. Two hours later, four huge company wagons loaded with men pulled up to the mine entrance. They had orders from Braxton to dig until they dropped. Just out of view, the church pianist sat in the back of Braxton's coach holding James' shotgun on Braxton. Within an hour, James was directing the digging. Knowing no one could dig all night, he divided the miners and Braxton's men into two groups. Each group dug for thirty minutes and rested ten. Daylight came and they were still digging. Just before noon on Sunday, they broke through into the mine. All fifteen men were rescued.

"James went to Braxton's coach and woke him up. 'Okay, Braxton,' he said. 'Nobody knows I forced you to help. You can call the sheriff on me or you can look like a hero. It's your choice.'

"A few minutes later, James delivered his Sunday morning sermon an hour late. The church was packed and so was the churchyard. On Monday morning, the mine opened as usual. On Tuesday,

Fayette County Sheriff Solomon Loofborrow showed up at the church. 'You come to arrest me, I guess,' James said.

"'No, I didn't,'" the sheriff replied. 'It occurred to me the best way to keep you from getting arrested is to appoint you as a deputy. Are you interested?' James thought about the offer for a few seconds. 'I'll take it if I don't have to quit preaching.' Sheriff Loofborrow agreed. A few minutes later, Reverend James McLean was also Deputy James McLean. Twelve years later, James was elected sheriff by popular demand. Every Sunday morning, he took off his uniform and climbed up on the pulpit. He often said that men elected him to be a sheriff but God elected him to be a preacher."

Christmas Prayer

Nellie Aldridge was born on December 25, 1912. The disadvantage of that birthdate was she invariably received only one present. She would open a small package to read, "Happy birthday, honey, and Merry Christmas." In her younger days, presents were few and far between so it really didn't make much difference. Early in the depression, she had married Ken Blankenship, and of course, in those days, things weren't much better. In the next decade, they had five children. They didn't have much in the way of material things, but they had lots of love and that was enough for Nellie. Still, when Ken bought her a birthday present, it also said Merry Christmas. Over the years, she had learned not to expect a different gift for each occasion.

As her children grew, she was always careful to make sure they received birthday presents and Christmas presents. She knew what it felt like to get only one present. Be that as it may, as her children matured, they took up their father's habit and bought Nellie one present for both occasions.

At the age of 42, Ken had a massive heart attack and died instantly. Fortunately, three of her children were grown and the two others were teenagers. Nellie struggled on without Ken, but she never became interested in another man. After several years, her children encouraged her to remarry, but she always said, "I'm a one-man woman."

Just before her 65th birthday, her oldest son died of a massive heart attack, leaving behind a wife and four children. Two years later, her oldest daughter died. By the time Nellie was 75; all five of her children had died of the same disease that had claimed their father. Her children had taken jobs in other states, so her fifteen grandchildren were scattered all over the map. She continued to remain healthy, but she had no one. On occasion, one of her grandchildren would turn up and visit for an hour or so. To combat her loneliness, she made friends and joined a bridge club.

Things stayed stable for the next twenty years, but finally, at age 95, she checked into a rest home. The employees in the rest home loved her but that didn't make up for family. She now had a long list of great-grandchildren but she rarely saw any of them. By her 98th birthday, they stopped coming altogether. Every night, she would pray, "Dear Lord, let me see some of my family before I die. No one came, of course, but Nellie kept the faith.

One night, one of the nurses heard her prayer. The next evening, the nurse came in and asked about her family. Nellie was happy to tell her all she knew. She finally admitted she had great-grandchildren whose name she didn't know. She also speculated she now had great-great-grandchildren. A few days later, the nurse offered to make Nellie a family tree to put on the wall by her bed. Of course, the nurse had another motive, but Nellie had no idea.

Christmas was now approaching, along with her 100th birthday. On Christmas Eve, Nellie prayed her usual prayer. And then she added, "Lord, time is running out, but I still believe you'll answer my prayer."

She had received a few Christmas cards and after her prayers, she got those out of her bedside drawer and read them all again. The nurse came in and found them lined up on her bed, but Nellie was asleep. She quietly gathered the cards and put them in the drawer where she knew Nellie kept them.

Christmas morning after Nellie had finished her breakfast tray, the nurse came in with a wheelchair. "Okay, Nellie, let's go for a ride." Nellie stared at her for a moment.

"I don't think so," she replied. "There's no point in it."

"Get out of that bed," the nurse said. "The employees are having a little Christmas party and all the residents are invited. You might as well get a move on."

Reluctantly, Nellie got out of bed and sat in the wheelchair. The nurse started pushing her down the hall. When the nurse pushed Nellie to the door of the lunchroom, she stopped.

"Okay, Nellie, I want you to put this blindfold on.

The girls have a little surprise for you." Nellie said nothing as the nurse wrapped the cloth around her head, covering her eyes. And then the nurse pushed the wheelchair into the room and stopped.

"Are you ready, Nellie?" she asked. Nellie nodded "yes." The nurse removed the blindfold.

When Nellie's eyes adjusted to the room, it took her a few moments to realize who the people standing in a semicircle were. The one in the center stepped forward.

"Merry Christmas and Happy Birthday, Grandma," he said. He had a package in each hand. Seven grandchildren stood on each side of him. All fifteen of them were there. There were about the same number of great-grandchildren and three of them were holding babies; Nellie's great-great-grandchildren.

They all walked forward and began hugging her, and of course, they all tried to talk at once. The party lasted for two hours and then Nellie began to tire out. She had opened presents until her arms hurt. The nurse pushed her back to her room escorted by her family entourage. They stayed in the room for a long time until they began to leave, one at a time. That night, Nellie said her prayers surrounded by piles of Christmas and birthday presents. "Thank you, Lord," Nellie prayed. "I'm ready to go any time you want to take me."

Next morning, the nurse came in and turned on the light. Nellie was lying on her back with a smile on her face. "All right, young lady," the nurse said. "It's time to rise and shine."

Nellie didn't move. It took the nurse a few mo-

ments to realize Nellie was dead. As was the rule, she
called in the doctor. He arrived an hour later, and
checked Nellie' pulse and heartbeat. There were none.

"Just as you thought, Nurse," he said. Nellie's
gone to her maker. You know, I believe this is the first
time I've ever seen a dead woman with a big smile on
her face."

EPILOGUE

Growing up in Nantahala

L ike the rest of Macon County, North Carolina, the Nantahala community was very different in the 1940's than it is today. Weaver Cochran had a thriving general store just around the corner from where the Nantahala School is now. People could barter by bringing in eggs, apples, berries and vegetables in season. They would take home sugar, salt, flour, fatback meat and other essentials. Too, they could buy on credit when necessary. Most people were honest and would repay Weaver when they could.

Most of the time, I went with Dad to buy grocery items we needed. When he could afford it, I would be treated to a Royal Crown Cola and a Moon Pie. Sometimes, I would get peanuts and pour them in my drink. I loved the salty taste. I can still close my eyes and imagine how good they tasted. In those days, kids weren't spoiled by having too much of everything they wanted.

Dad and I would walk down Camp Branch Road

to Union Hill Baptist Church and then cut across the mountain trail that came out at the intersection of Hampton Branch Road. The total trip was about three miles. We would go back the same route. Dad usually carried a fifty pound bag of flour, cornmeal or feed on his right shoulder and a bag of groceries in his left hand. I would carry a small bag of groceries.

We usually stopped to rest when I got tired. Just recently, I tried to carry a fifty pound bag of Sakrete two trips around the house. I was tired before I completed the second circuit. Knowing that, it's difficult to understand how my dad carried all that weight three miles across the mountain. Aside from the fact that he was stronger than I am, he really had no choice. We had no car and no horse.

I remember one year in particular, Dad sharecropped a big field of corn from Ervin Grant. I would go with him to hoe the corn. We would leave out at dawn and return at dusk. I would help dad for a while and then sneak off to the lake to fish. I think he let me get away with it because I usually caught something, and then we would have fresh fish for supper. Dad taught me how to clean the fish and after I finished, I would take them to the little stream at the edge of the yard and wash them off. Mom would salt and pepper the fish and then roll them in cornmeal. We would have potatoes and another vegetable with the fish if we had it. Naturally, we had cornbread, my favorite bread in the entire world.

In those days, almost everybody went to church. There were four churches, and they were all Baptist. I didn't know there were other denominations until we moved to Burke County. We went to Union Hill, but occasionally we would go to Happy Top, Briartown or Bethel Hill. Every church had a reunion, so if we worked it right, we could go to all four. The reunions (or decorations) gave the ladies a chance to show off their cooking skills which were considerable. I don't think there was a bad cook in the entire Nantahala Community. Eating has always been one of my favorite sports.

Today, farming in Nantahala has dwindled to practically nothing. In the 1940's, farms were neat, orderly and productive. Crops and gardens were well tended, milk cows grazed on the hillsides along with oxen, horses and mules. Every farm had at least one hog that was fed table scraps, assuming the dogs didn't get them first. Chickens roamed freely, and kids made a game out of hunting the eggs. I guess one could say that we had an Easter egg hunt every week except they weren't colored.

Families rose before dawn, ate breakfast and immediately began their chores. Kids had work to do before they went to school. Cows had to be milked; hogs, chickens and livestock had to be fed. During planting and harvesting, kids were kept home from school to work in the fields.

We would get together with Grandma Rosa and Uncle John and hoe our corn. Whoever was fastest hoed the bottom row and so on until everyone had a place. This was done to keep a faster person from covering up the next row down before it got hoed. Sometimes we would have a hoeing contest to see who was the fastest. Try as I might, I couldn't beat Uncle John.

He was like a one-man tractor.

In the fall, hogs were killed, scraped, cleaned, cut up, salted down and stored in the smoke house. Again, everyone pitched in and helped. We all had an assigned job, and there was no shirking our duty. Uncle John would cut up and joke, but he insisted on keeping up the pace. And of course, we all looked forward to all that fresh pork. For breakfast, Grandma or Mom would fry fresh sausage to go with our eggs. Sometimes we had a big slice of ham. Occasionally, Dad would buy some beef, and Mom would stew it. I would sit and lick my lips when the delicious smell wafted from the kitchen.

Apples, onions and potatoes were stored in holes in the ground or in storage bins. I can remember scratching away the snow and digging out a few apples so Mom could cook stewed apples or make a cobbler. When we lived above Grandma Emma, we hauled pumpkins on sleds and stored them on hay in a building beside the barn. I once sat on top of a pumpkin that filled an entire sled.

At Thanksgiving, Dad and Uncle Truman would dig a big pumpkin out of the hay, slice and gut it and take it to the kitchen so the experts could perform their magic. My Aunt Winnie could make a pie to die for.

In those days, almost everything was organic. Cow manure was hauled out of the barn and spread on the garden. Nothing was wasted. Corn had to be stored in the crib for later feeding to the livestock or shucked, shelled and taken to the grist mill for grinding into corn meal. And of course, canning had to be done as the vegetables and fruits became available. Pint and quart jars were a valuable commodity and were treated with tender loving care. When they were emptied of their contents, usually during winter, they were washed and stored away for next year's canning.

Johnny Appleseed must have passed through Nantahala because every farm had lots of apple trees. Of course, there were cooking apples and eating apples. Jonathon, McIntosh, Golden Delicious, Winesap, Granny Smith and many other types grew in abundance. In the fall, we gathered apples as they fell from the trees. Since I was agile as a monkey, I would climb the trees and shake them out while the women gathered them in their aprons or in baskets.

Apples were another staple to help make it through the winter. One of the greatest smells in the world was a fresh apple pie cooling in the window. Of course women had to be careful about that because a bear can smell an apple pie ten miles away. And of course, there was apple butter. Nothing tastes better than homemade apple butter except more homemade apple butter. Once, my cousin Shirley Jean and I got caught in Grandma's cellar with an open quart and one spoon between us. Naturally, by the time Grandma found us, the jar was almost empty.

If anyone in Nantahala had a tractor in those days, I'm not aware of it. Grain and hay were cut with a mowing scythe. It took a strong and hardy man to swing a scythe from daylight to dark. Once dried in the fields, the hay had to be raked and stacked. I once stacked hay all day for Alexander McMahan for ten cents. That wasn't much money for all that work.

Another job I enjoyed was bringing in the cow or cows for milking. I would select a good stick, go up in the pasture and drive the cows to the barn or shed. Some of them had a mind of their own and would try to run away. I would have to run fast, out flank them and start them out again. I always succeeded, but sometimes I was worn out by the time I got the job done.

Every adult has their favorite memories of childhood days. Some kids are born with a silver spoon in their mouth and others, like me, are born poor. As my cousin Gail says, "In the 1940's in Nantahala, everybody was poor so we didn't know the difference."

The Bible says we shall not covet, and I don't remember doing any of that. We didn't have much, but we certainly didn't desire anyone else's worldly possessions. My parents were warm and loving, and they raised us kids to be the same. We may have been poor economically, but we were rich in everything else. Certainly, it's preferable to being shipped off to a military or boarding school by a couple of wealthy parents. I, for one, would rather have love than money. Life is short, and there isn't a lot of love in it. Thanks to my wealthy parents, I've had lots of love to pass on to my kids. My sons are not ashamed to say they love me, and my grandkids do the same.

As a wise man once said, "When life gives you love, embrace it; take it in, make it every part of you, but don't be too hasty, for haste can scare love away. Take it slow and let everything happen as it will. True love lies in the future of those who follow this doctrine." It doesn't get any better than that.